Glencoe

Algebra 2

Integration
Applications
Connections

Enrichment Masters

GLENCOE
McGraw-Hill

New York, New York   Columbus, Ohio   Woodland Hills, California   Peoria, Illinois

Glencoe/McGraw-Hill

*A Division of The **McGraw·Hill** Companies*

Send all inquiries to:
Glencoe/McGraw-Hill
936 Eastwind Drive
Westerville, OH 43081

Algebra 2
Enrichment Masters

ISBN: 0-02-825156-3

4 5 6 7 8 9 10   024   03 02 01 00 99 98

Contents

Enrichment

Continued Fractions

The fraction below is an example of a continued fraction. Note that each fraction in the continued fraction has a numerator of 1.

$$2 + \cfrac{1}{3 + \cfrac{1}{4 + \cfrac{1}{5}}}$$

Example 1:

Evaluate the continued fraction above. Start at the bottom and work your way up.

Step 1: $4 + \dfrac{1}{5} = \dfrac{20}{5} + \dfrac{1}{5} = \dfrac{21}{5}$

Step 2: $\dfrac{1}{\frac{21}{5}} = \dfrac{5}{21}$

Step 3: $3 + \dfrac{5}{21} = \dfrac{63}{21} + \dfrac{5}{21} = \dfrac{68}{21}$

Step 4: $\dfrac{1}{\frac{68}{21}} = \dfrac{21}{68}$

Step 5: $2 + \dfrac{21}{68} = 2\dfrac{21}{68}$

Example 2:

Change $\dfrac{25}{11}$ into a continued fraction. Follow the steps.

Step 1: $\dfrac{25}{11} = \dfrac{22}{11} + \dfrac{3}{11} = 2 + \dfrac{3}{11}$

Step 2: $\dfrac{3}{11} = \dfrac{1}{\frac{11}{3}}$

Step 3: $\dfrac{11}{3} = \dfrac{9}{3} + \dfrac{2}{3} = 3 + \dfrac{2}{3}$

Step 4: $\dfrac{2}{3} = \dfrac{1}{\frac{3}{2}}$

Step 5: $\dfrac{3}{2} = \dfrac{2}{2} + \dfrac{1}{2} = 1 + \dfrac{1}{2}$

Stop, because the numerator is 1.

Thus, $\dfrac{25}{11}$ can be written as $2 + \cfrac{1}{3 + \cfrac{1}{1 + \cfrac{1}{2}}}$

Evaluate each continued fraction.

1. $1 + \cfrac{1}{1 + \cfrac{1}{2 + \cfrac{1}{2 + \cfrac{1}{3}}}}$

2. $0 + \cfrac{1}{6 + \cfrac{1}{4 + \cfrac{1}{2}}}$

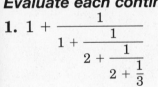

3. $2 + \cfrac{1}{4 + \cfrac{1}{6 + \cfrac{1}{8 + \cfrac{1}{10}}}}$

4. $5 + \cfrac{1}{7 + \cfrac{1}{9 + \cfrac{1}{11}}}$

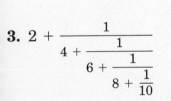

Change each fraction into a continued fraction.

5. $\dfrac{75}{31}$

6. $\dfrac{29}{8}$

7. $\dfrac{13}{19}$

Algebra 2

Enrichment

Continued Fractions

The fraction below is an example of a continued fraction. Note that each fraction in the continued fraction has a numerator of 1.

$$2 + \cfrac{1}{3 + \cfrac{1}{4 + \cfrac{1}{5}}}$$

Example 1:

Evaluate the continued fraction above. Start at the bottom and work your way up.

Step 1: $4 + \dfrac{1}{5} = \dfrac{20}{5} + \dfrac{1}{5} = \dfrac{21}{5}$

Step 2: $\dfrac{1}{\frac{21}{5}} = \dfrac{5}{21}$

Step 3: $3 + \dfrac{5}{21} = \dfrac{63}{21} + \dfrac{5}{21} = \dfrac{68}{21}$

Step 4: $\dfrac{1}{\frac{68}{21}} = \dfrac{21}{68}$

Step 5: $2 + \dfrac{21}{68} = 2\dfrac{21}{68}$

Example 2:

Change $\dfrac{25}{11}$ into a continued fraction. Follow the steps.

Step 1: $\dfrac{25}{11} = \dfrac{22}{11} + \dfrac{3}{11} = 2 + \dfrac{3}{11}$

Step 2: $\dfrac{3}{11} = \dfrac{1}{\frac{11}{3}}$

Step 3: $\dfrac{11}{3} = \dfrac{9}{3} + \dfrac{2}{3} = 3 + \dfrac{2}{3}$

Step 4: $\dfrac{2}{3} = \dfrac{1}{\frac{3}{2}}$

Step 5: $\dfrac{3}{2} = \dfrac{2}{2} + \dfrac{1}{2} = 1 + \dfrac{1}{2}$

Stop, because the numerator is 1.

Thus, $\dfrac{25}{11}$ can be written as $2 + \cfrac{1}{3 + \cfrac{1}{1 + \cfrac{1}{2}}}$

Evaluate each continued fraction.

1. $1 + \cfrac{1}{1 + \cfrac{1}{2 + \cfrac{1}{2 + \frac{1}{3}}}}$ $\quad 1\dfrac{17}{24}$

2. $0 + \cfrac{1}{6 + \cfrac{1}{4 + \frac{1}{2}}}$ $\quad \dfrac{9}{56}$

3. $2 + \cfrac{1}{4 + \cfrac{1}{6 + \cfrac{1}{8 + \frac{1}{10}}}}$ $\quad 2\dfrac{496}{2065}$

4. $5 + \cfrac{1}{7 + \cfrac{1}{9 + \frac{1}{11}}}$ $\quad 5\dfrac{100}{711}$

Change each fraction into a continued fraction.

5. $\dfrac{75}{31}$

$2 + \cfrac{1}{2 + \cfrac{1}{2 + \cfrac{1}{1 + \cfrac{1}{1 + \frac{1}{2}}}}}$

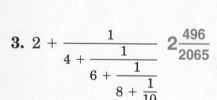

6. $\dfrac{29}{8}$

$3 + \cfrac{1}{1 + \cfrac{1}{1 + \cfrac{1}{1 + \frac{1}{2}}}}$

7. $\dfrac{13}{19}$

$0 + \cfrac{1}{1 + \cfrac{1}{2 + \frac{1}{6}}}$

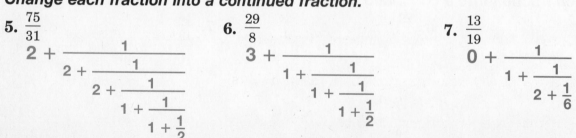

Enrichment

Equivalence Relations

A relation R on a set A is an *equivalence relation* if it has the following properties.

Reflexive Property	For any element a of set A, a R a.
Symmetric Property	For all elements a and b of set A, if a R b, then b R a.
Transitive Property	For all elements a, b, and c of set A, if a R b and b R c, then a R c.

Equality on the set of all real numbers is reflexive, symmetric, and transitive. Therefore, it is an equivalence relation.

In each of the following, a relation and a set are given. Write yes if the relation is an equivalence relation on the given set. If it is not, tell which of the properties it fails to exhibit.

1. $<$, {all numbers}

2. $\cong$, {all triangles in a plane}

3. is the sister of, {all women in Tennessee}

4. $\geq$, {all numbers}

5. is a factor of, {all nonzero integers}

6. $\sim$, {all polygons in a plane}

7. is the spouse of, {all people in Roanoke, Virginia}

8. $\perp$, {all lines in a plane}

9. is a multiple of, {all integers}

10. is the square of, {all numbers}

11. $\parallel$, {all lines in a plane}

12. has the same color eyes as,
    {all members of the Cleveland Symphony Orchestra}

13. is the greatest integer not greater than, {all numbers}

14. is the greatest integer not greater than, {all integers}

Equivalence Relations

A relation R on a set A is an *equivalence relation* if it has the following properties.

Reflexive Property	For any element a of set A, a R a.
Symmetric Property	For all elements a and b of set A, if a R b, then b R a.
Transitive Property	For all elements a, b, and c of set A, if a R b and b R c, then a R c.

Equality on the set of all real numbers is reflexive, symmetric, and transitive. Therefore, it is an equivalence relation.

In each of the following, a relation and a set are given. Write yes if the relation is an equivalence relation on the given set. If it is not, tell which of the properties it fails to exhibit.

1. $<$, {all numbers} **no; reflexive, symmetric**

2. $\cong$, {all triangles in a plane} **yes**

3. is the sister of, {all women in Tennessee} **no; reflexive**

4. $\geq$, {all numbers} **no; symmetric**

5. is a factor of, {all nonzero integers} **no; symmetric**

6. $\sim$, {all polygons in a plane} **yes**

7. is the spouse of, {all people in Roanoke, Virginia} **no; reflexive, transitive**

8. $\perp$, {all lines in a plane} **no; reflexive, transitive**

9. is a multiple of, {all integers} **no; symmetric**

10. is the square of, {all numbers} **no; reflexive, symmetric, transitive**

11. $\parallel$, {all lines in a plane} **no; reflexive**

12. has the same color eyes as, {all members of the Cleveland Symphony Orchestra} **yes**

13. is the greatest integer not greater than, {all numbers} **no; reflexive, symmetric, transitive**

14. is the greatest integer not greater than, {all integers} **yes**

Algebra 2

NAME_____ DATE _____

Enrichment

Misuses of Statistics

Statistics can be misleading. Graphs for a set of data can look very different from one another. Compare the following graphs.

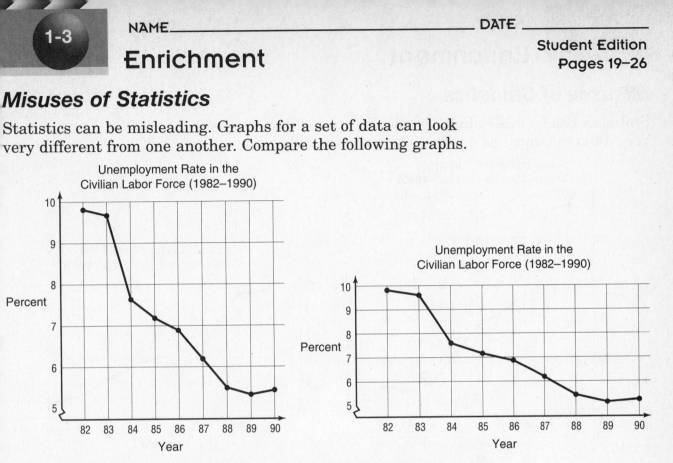

Notice that the two graphs show the same data, but the spacing in the vertical and horizontal scales differs. Scales can be cramped or spread out to make a graph that gives a certain impression. Which graph would you use to give the impression that the unemployment rate dropped dramatically from 1983 to 1990?

Suppose that a car company claims, "75% of people surveyed say that our car is better than the competition." If four people were asked which car they preferred and 75% agreed, how many people thought that *Our Car* was better?

The advertisement was misleading in other ways as well. For example, who was surveyed—were the people company employees, or impartial buyers?

Suppose an advertiser claims that 90% of all of one brand of car sold in the last 10 years are still on the road.

1. If 10,000 cars were sold, how many are still on the road?

2. If 1000 cars were sold, how many are still on the road?

3. Find an example to show how you think averages could be used in a misleading way.

4. A survey of a large sample of people who own small computers revealed that 85% of the people thought the instruction manuals should be better written. A manufacturer of small computers claimed that it surveyed many of the same people and found that all of them liked their manuals. Discuss the possible discrepancy in the results.

Algebra 2

Enrichment

Misuses of Statistics

Statistics can be misleading. Graphs for a set of data can look very different from one another. Compare the following graphs.

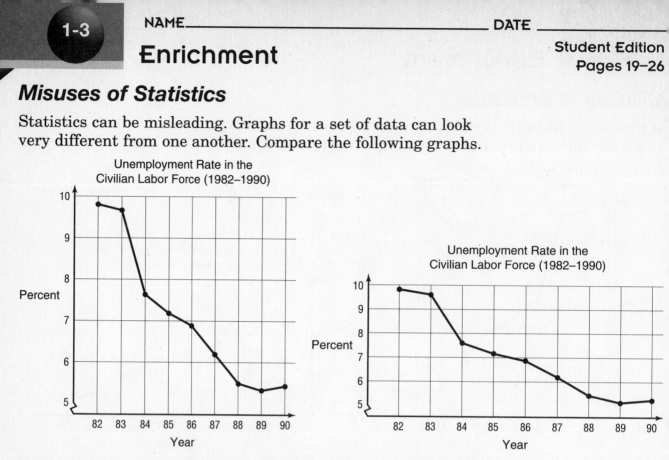

Notice that the two graphs show the same data, but the spacing in the vertical and horizontal scales differs. Scales can be cramped or spread out to make a graph that gives a certain impression. Which graph would you use to give the impression that the unemployment rate dropped dramatically from 1983 to 1990? **the first graph**

Suppose that a car company claims, "75% of people surveyed say that our car is better than the competition." If four people were asked which car they preferred and 75% agreed, how many people thought that *Our Car* was better? **3 people**

The advertisement was misleading in other ways as well. For example, who was surveyed—were the people company employees, or impartial buyers?

Suppose an advertiser claims that 90% of all of one brand of car sold in the last 10 years are still on the road.

1. If 10,000 cars were sold, how many are still on the road? **9,000**

2. If 1000 cars were sold, how many are still on the road? **900**

3. Find an example to show how you think averages could be used in a misleading way. **See students' work.**

4. A survey of a large sample of people who own small computers revealed that 85% of the people thought the instruction manuals should be better written. A manufacturer of small computers claimed that it surveyed many of the same people and found that all of them liked their manuals. Discuss the possible discrepancy in the results. **See students' work.**

1-4

Enrichment

Significant Digits

All measurements are approximations. The **significant digits**
of an approximate number are those which indicate the results
of a measurement. For example, the mass of an object, measured
to the nearest gram, is 210 grams. The measurement 21<u>0</u> g has
3 significant digits. The mass of the same object, measured to
the nearest 100 g, is 200 g. The measurement 200 g has one
significant digit.

1. Nonzero digits and zeros between significant digits are
   significant. For example, the measurement 9.071 m has
   4 significant digits, 9, 0, 7, and 1.

2. Zeros at the end of a decimal fraction are significant. The
   measurement 0.050 mm has 2 significant digits, 5 and 0.

3. Underlined zeros in whole numbers are significant. The
   measurement 104,0<u>0</u>0 km has 5 significant digits, 1, 0, 4, 0,
   and 0.

In general, a computation involving multiplication or division of
measurements *cannot* be more accurate than the least accurate
measurement in the computation. Thus, the result of computation
involving multiplication or division of measurements should be
rounded to the number of significant digits in the least accurate
measurement.

Example: The mass of 37 quarters if 21<u>0</u> g. Find the mass of one quarter.

$$\text{mass of 1 quarter} = 21\underline{0} \text{ g} \div 37$$ 21<u>0</u> has 3 significant digits.
                                                                      37 does not represent a measurement.
$$= 5.68 \text{ g}$$ Round the result to 3 significant digits.
                        Why?

Write the number of significant digits for each measurement.

1. 8314.20 m   2. 30.70 cm   3. 0.01 mm   4. 0.0605 mg

5. 37<u>0</u>,000 km   6. 370,0<u>0</u>0 km   7. 9.7×10^4 g   8. 3.20×10^{-2} g

Solve. Round each result to the correct number of significant digits.

9. 23 m × 1.54 m   10. 12,0<u>0</u>0 ft ÷ 52<u>0</u> ft   11. 2.5 cm × 25

12. 11.01 mm × 11   13. 908 yd ÷ 0.5   14. 38.6 m × 4.0 m

NAME_____ DATE _____

Enrichment

Significant Digits

All measurements are approximations. The **significant digits** of an approximate number are those which indicate the results of a measurement. For example, the mass of an object, measured to the nearest gram, is 210 grams. The measurement 210 g has 3 significant digits. The mass of the same object, measured to the nearest 100 g, is 200 g. The measurement 200 g has one significant digit.

1. Nonzero digits and zeros between significant digits are significant. For example, the measurement 9.071 m has 4 significant digits, 9, 0, 7, and 1.

2. Zeros at the end of a decimal fraction are significant. The measurement 0.050 mm has 2 significant digits, 5 and 0.

3. Underlined zeros in whole numbers are significant. The measurement 104,0̲0̲0 km has 5 significant digits, 1, 0, 4, 0, and 0.

In general, a computation involving multiplication or division of measurements *cannot* be more accurate than the least accurate measurement in the computation. Thus, the result of computation involving multiplication or division of measurements should be rounded to the number of significant digits in the least accurate measurement.

Example: The mass of 37 quarters if 21̲0 g. Find the mass of one quarter.

mass of 1 quarter = 21̲0 g ÷ 37   21̲0 has 3 significant digits.
                                      37 does not represent a measurement.
             = 5.68 g   Round the result to 3 significant digits.
                                      Why?

Write the number of significant digits for each measurement.

1. 8314.20 m
   6

2. 30.70 cm
   4

3. 0.01 mm
   1

4. 0.0605 mg
   3

5. 37̲0,000 km
   3

6. 370,0̲0̲0 km
   5

7. 9.7×10^4 g
   2

8. 3.20×10^{-2} g
   3

Solve. Round each result to the correct number of significant digits.

9. 23 m × 1.54 m
   35 m²

10. 12,000 ft ÷ 52̲0 ft
    23.1̄

11. 2.5 cm × 25
    63 cm

12. 11.01 mm × 11
    121.1 mm

13. 908 yd ÷ 0.5
    1820 yd

14. 38.6 m × 4.0 m
    150 m²

Algebra 2

NAME_____ DATE_____

Enrichment

Venn Diagrams

Relationships among sets can be shown using Venn diagrams. Study the diagrams below. The circles represent sets A and B, which are subsets of set S.

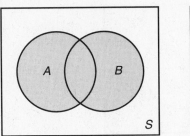 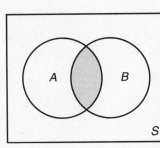 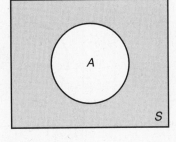

The union of A and B consists of all elements in *either* A or B.
The intersection of A and B consists of all elements in *both* A and B.
The complement of A consists of all elements *not* in A.

You can combine the operations of union, intersection, and finding the complement.

Example: Shade the region $(A \cap B)'$.

$(A \cap B)'$ means the complement of the intersection of A and B.
First find the intersection of A and B.
Then find its complement.

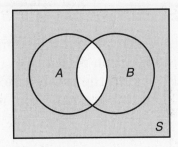

Draw a Venn diagram and shade the region indicated.

1. $A' \cap B$

2. $A' \cup B$

3. $A' \cap B'$

4. $A' \cup B'$

5. $(A \cup B)'$

6. $A \cap B'$

Draw a Venn diagram and three overlapping circles. Then shade the region indicated.

7. $(A \cup B) \cup C'$

8. $(A \cup B)' \cap C'$

9. $A \cup (B \cup C)$

10. $(A \cup B) \cup C$

11. Is the union operation associative? _____

12. Is the intersection operation associative? _____

5

NAME_____ DATE _____

Enrichment

Venn Diagrams

Relationships among sets can be shown using Venn diagrams. Study the diagrams below. The circles represent sets A and B, which are subsets of set S.

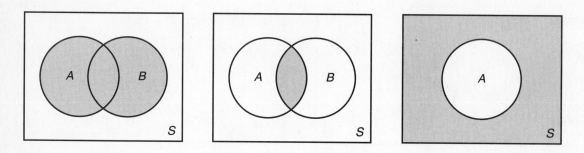

The union of A and B consists of all elements in *either* A or B.
The intersection of A and B consists of all elements in *both* A and B.
The complement of A consists of all elements *not* in A.

You can combine the operations of union, intersection, and finding the complement.

Example: Shade the region $(A \cap B)'$.

$(A \cap B)'$ means the complement of the intersection of A and B.
First find the intersection of A and B.
Then find its complement.

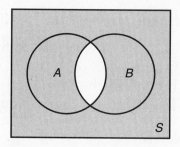

Draw a Venn diagram and shade the region indicated. See students' diagrams.

1. $A' \cap B$

2. $A' \cup B$

3. $A' \cap B'$

4. $A' \cup B'$

5. $(A \cup B)'$

6. $A \cap B'$

Draw a Venn diagram and three overlapping circles. Then shade the region indicated. See students' diagrams.

7. $(A \cup B) \cup C'$

8. $(A \cup B)' \cap C'$

9. $A \cup (B \cup C)$

10. $(A \cup B) \cup C$

11. Is the union operation associative? yes

12. Is the intersection operation associative? yes

Algebra 2

NAME_____ DATE _____

Enrichment

Properties of a Group

A set of numbers forms a group with respect to an operation if for that operation the set has (1) the closure property, (2) the associative property, (3) a member which is an identity, and (4) an inverse for each member of the set.

Example 1: Does the set $\{0, 1, 2, 3, \cdots\}$ form a group with respect to addition?

Closure property: For all numbers in the set, is $a + b$ in the set?
$0 + 1 = 1$, and 1 is in the set; $0 + 2 = 2$, and 2 is in the set; and so on.
The set has closure for addition.

Associative property: For all numbers in the set, does $a + (b + c) = (a + b) + c$?
$0 + (1 + 2) = (0 + 1) + 2$;
$1 + (2 + 3) = (1 + 2) + 3$; and so on.
The set is associative for addition.

Identity: Is there some number, i, in the set such that $i + a = a = a + i$ for all a?
$0 + 1 = 1 = 1 + 0$; $0 + 2 = 2 = 2 + 0$; and so on.
The identity for addition is 0.

Inverse: Does each number, a, have an inverse, a', such that $a' + a = a + a' = i$?
The integer inverse of 3 is -3 since $-3 + 3 = 0$, and 0 is the identity for addition. But the set does not contain -3. Therefore, there is no inverse for 3.

The set is not a group with respect to addition because only three of the four properties hold.

Example 2: Is the set $\{-1, 1\}$ a group with respect to multiplication?

Closure property: $(-1)(-1) = 1$; $(-1)(1) = -1$; $(1)(-1) = -1$; $(1)(1) = 1$
The set has closure for multiplication.

Associative property: $(-1)[(-1)(-1)] = (-1)(1) = -1$; and so on
The set is associative for multiplication.

Identity: $1(-1) = -1$; $1(1) = 1$
The identity for multiplication is 1.

Inverse: -1 is the inverse of -1 since $(-1)(-1) = 1$, and 1 is the identity.
1 is the inverse of 1 since $(1)(1) = 1$, and 1 is the identity.
Each member has an inverse.

The set $\{-1, 1\}$ is a group with respect to multiplication because all four properties hold.

Tell whether the set forms a group with respect to the given operation.

1. {integers}, addition _____

2. {integers}, multiplication _____

3. $\left\{\dfrac{1}{2}, \dfrac{2}{2}, \dfrac{3}{2}, \cdots\right\}$, addition _____

4. {multiples of 5}, multiplication _____

5. $\{x, x^2, x^3, x^4, \cdots\}$ addition _____

6. $\{\sqrt{1}, \sqrt{2}, \sqrt{3}, \cdots\}$, multiplication _____

7. {irrational numbers}, addition _____

8. {rational numbers}, addition _____

Enrichment

Properties of a Group

A set of numbers forms a group with respect to an operation if
for that operation the set has (1) the closure property, (2) the
associative property, (3) a member which is an identity, and
(4) an inverse for each member of the set.

Example 1: Does the set $\{0, 1, 2, 3, \cdots\}$ form a group with respect to addition?

Closure property: For all numbers in the set, is $a + b$ in the set?
$0 + 1 = 1$, and 1 is in the set; $0 + 2 = 2$, and 2 is in the set; and so on.
The set has closure for addition.

Associative property: For all numbers in the set, does $a + (b + c) = (a + b) + c$?
$0 + (1 + 2) = (0 + 1) + 2$;
$1 + (2 + 3) = (1 + 2) + 3$; and so on.
The set is associative for addition.

Identity: Is there some number, i, in the set such that $i + a = a = a + i$ for all a?
$0 + 1 = 1 = 1 + 0$; $0 + 2 = 2 = 2 + 0$; and so on.
The identity for addition is 0.

Inverse: Does each number, a, have an inverse, a', such that $a' + a = a + a' = i$?
The integer inverse of 3 is -3 since $-3 + 3 = 0$, and 0 is the identity for addition. But the set does not contain -3. Therefore, there is no inverse for 3.

The set is not a group with respect to addition because only three of the four properties hold.

Example 2: Is the set $\{-1, 1\}$ a group with respect to multiplication?

Closure property: $(-1)(-1) = 1$; $(-1)(1) = -1$; $(1)(-1) = -1$; $(1)(1) = 1$
The set has closure for multiplication.

Associative property: $(-1)[(-1)(-1)] = (-1)(1) = -1$; and so on
The set is associative for multiplication.

Identity: $1(-1) = -1$; $1(1) = 1$
The identity for multiplication is 1.

Inverse: -1 is the inverse of -1 since $(-1)(-1) = 1$, and 1 is the identity.
1 is the inverse of 1 since $(1)(1) = 1$, and 1 is the identity.
Each member has an inverse.

The set $\{-1, 1\}$ is a group with respect to multiplication because all four properties hold.

Tell whether the set forms a group with respect to the given operation.

1. {integers}, addition ___yes___

2. {integers}, multiplication ___no___

3. $\left\{\frac{1}{2}, \frac{2}{2}, \frac{3}{2}, \cdots\right\}$, addition ___no___

4. {multiples of 5}, multiplication ___no___

5. $\{x, x^2, x^3, x^4, \cdots\}$ addition ___no___

6. $\{\sqrt{1}, \sqrt{2}, \sqrt{3}, \cdots\}$, multiplication ___no___

7. {irrational numbers}, addition ___no___

8. {rational numbers}, addition ___yes___

Enrichment

Conjunctions and Disjunctions

An absolute value inequality may be solved as a compound sentence.

Example: Solve $|2x| < 10$.

$|2x| < 10$ means $2x < 10$ and $2x > -10$.

Solve each inequality. $x < 5$ and $x > -5$.

Every solution for $|2x| < 10$ is a replacement for x that makes both $x < 5$ and $x > -5$ true.

A compound sentence that combines two statements by the word *and* is a *conjunction*.

Example: Solve $|3x - 7| \geq 11$.

$|3x - 7| \geq 11$ means $3x - 7 \geq 11$ or $3x - 7 \leq -11$.

Solve each inequality. $3x \geq 18$ or $3x \leq -4$

$$x \geq 6 \text{ or } x \leq -\frac{4}{3}$$

Every solution for the inequality is a replacement for x that makes either $x \geq 6$ or $x \leq -\frac{4}{3}$ true.

A compound sentence that combines two statements by the word *or* is a *disjunction*.

Solve each inequality. Then write whether the solution is a conjunction or disjunction.

1. $|4x| > 24$

2. $|x - 7| \leq 8$

3. $|2x + 5| < 1$

4. $|x - 1| \geq 1$

5. $|3x - 1| \leq x$

6. $7 - |2x| > 5$

7. $\left|\frac{x}{2} + 1\right| \geq 7$

8. $\left|\frac{x - 4}{3}\right| < 4$

9. $|8 - x| > 2$

10. $|5 - 2x| \leq 3$

Enrichment

Conjunctions and Disjunctions

An absolute value inequality may be solved as a compound sentence.

Example: Solve $|2x| < 10$.

$|2x| < 10$ means $2x < 10$ and $2x > -10$.

Solve each inequality. $x < 5$ and $x > -5$.

Every solution for $|2x| < 10$ is a replacement for x that makes both $x < 5$ and $x > -5$ true.

A compound sentence that combines two statements by the word *and* is a *conjunction*.

Example: Solve $|3x - 7| \geq 11$.

$|3x - 7| \geq 11$ means $3x - 7 \geq 11$ or $3x - 7 \leq -11$.

Solve each inequality. $3x \geq 18$ or $3x \leq -4$

$$x \geq 6 \text{ or } x \leq -\frac{4}{3}$$

Every solution for the inequality is a replacement for x that makes either $x \geq 6$ or $x \leq -\frac{4}{3}$ true.

A compound sentence that combines two statements by the word *or* is a *disjunction*.

Solve each inequality. Then write whether the solution is a conjunction or disjunction.

1. $|4x| > 24$
   $x > 6$ or $x < -6$; disjunction

2. $|x - 7| \leq 8$
   $x \leq 15$ and $x \geq -1$; conjunction

3. $|2x + 5| < 1$
   $x < -2$ and $x > -3$; conjunction

4. $|x - 1| \geq 1$
   $x \geq 2$ or $x \leq 0$; disjunction

5. $|3x - 1| \leq x$
   $x \leq \frac{1}{2}$ and $x \geq \frac{1}{4}$; conjunction

6. $7 - |2x| > 5$
   $x < 1$ and $x > -1$; conjunction

7. $\left|\frac{x}{2} + 1\right| \geq 7$
   $x \geq 12$ or $x \leq -16$; disjunction

8. $\left|\frac{x - 4}{3}\right| < 4$
   $x < 16$ and $x > -8$; conjunction

9. $|8 - x| > 2$
   $x < 6$ or $x > 10$; disjunction

10. $|5 - 2x| \leq 3$
    $x \geq 1$ and $x \leq 4$; conjunction

Mappings

There are three special ways in which one set can be mapped to another. A set can be mapped *into* another set, *onto* another set, or can have a *one-to-one correspondence* with another set.

Definition of an into mapping	A mapping from set *A* to set *B* is an *into* mapping if every element of *A* is mapped to one or more elements of set *B*, but never to an element not in *B*.
Definition of an onto mapping	A mapping from set *A* to set *B* is an *onto* mapping if each element of set *B* has at least one element of set *A* mapped to it.
Definition of a one-to-one correspondence	A mapping from set *A* onto set *B* is a *one-to-one correspondence* if each element of set *A* is mapped to exactly one element of set *B* and different elements of *A* are never mapped to the same element of *B*.

State whether each set is mapped into the second set, onto the second set, or has a one-to-one correspondence with the second set.

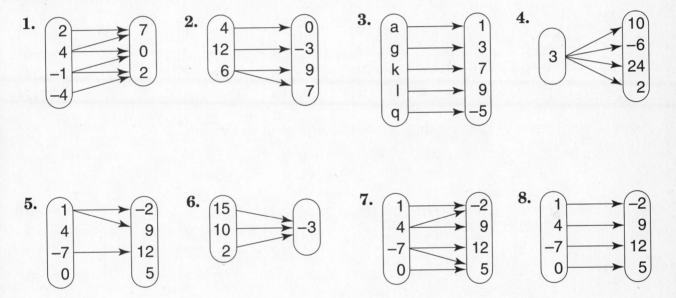

9. Can a set be mapped *onto* a set with fewer elements than it has?

10. Can a set be mapped *into* a set that has more elements than it has?

11. If a mapping from set *A* into set *B* is a one-to-one correspondence, what can you conclude about the number of elements in *A* and *B*?

Enrichment

Mappings

There are three special ways in which one set can be mapped to another. A set can be mapped *into* another set, *onto* another set, or can have a *one-to-one correspondence* with another set.

Definition of an into mapping	A mapping from set *A* to set *B* is an *into* mapping if every element of *A* is mapped to one or more elements of set *B*, but never to an element not in *B*.
Definition of an onto mapping	A mapping from set *A* to set *B* is an *onto* mapping if each element of set *B* has at least one element of set *A* mapped to it.
Definition of a one-to-one correspondence	A mapping from set *A* onto set *B* is a *one-to-one correspondence* if each element of set *A* is mapped to exactly one element of set *B* and different elements of *A* are never mapped to the same element of *B*.

State whether each set is mapped into the second set, onto the second set, or has a one-to-one correspondence with the second set.

1.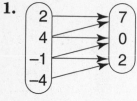

into, onto

2.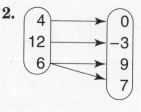

into, onto

3.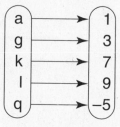

into, onto,
one-to-one

4.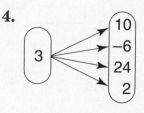

into, onto

5.

into

6.

into, onto

7.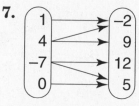

into, onto

8.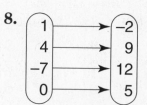

into, onto,
one-to-one

9. Can a set be mapped *onto* a set with fewer elements than it has? **yes**

10. Can a set be mapped *into* a set that has more elements than it has? **yes**

11. If a mapping from set *A* into set *B* is a one-to-one correspondence, what can you conclude about the number of elements in *A* and *B*? **The sets have the same number of elements.**

Algebra 2

Greatest Common Factor

Suppose we are given a linear equation $ax + by = c$ where a, b, and c are nonzero integers, and we want to know if there exist *integers x and y* that satisfy the equation. We could try guessing a few ˆtimes, but this process would be time consuming for an equation such as $588x + 432y = 72$. By using the Euclidean Algorithm, we can determine not only if such integers x and y exist, but also find them. The following example shows how this algorithm works.

Example: Find integers x and y that satisfy $588x + 432y = 72$.

Divide the greater of the two coefficients by the lesser to get a quotient and remainder. Then, repeat the process by dividing the divisor by the remainder until you get a remainder of 0. The process can be written as follows.

$$588 = 432(1) + 156 \qquad (1)$$
$$432 = 156(2) + 120 \qquad (2)$$
$$156 = 120(1) + 36 \qquad (3)$$
$$120 = 36(3) + 12 \qquad (4)$$
$$36 = 12(3)$$

The last nonzero remainder is the GCF of the two coefficients. If the constant term 72 is divisible by the GCF, then integers x and y do exist that satisfy the equation. To find x and y, work backward in the following manner.

$$72 = 6 \cdot 12$$
$$= 6 \cdot [120 - 36(3)] \qquad \text{substitute for 12 using (4)}$$
$$= 6(120) - 18(36)$$
$$= 6(120) - 18[156 - 120(1)] \qquad \text{substitute for 36 using (3)}$$
$$= -18(156) + 24(120)$$
$$= -18(156) + 24[432 - 156(2)] \qquad \text{substitute for 120 using (2)}$$
$$= 24(432) - 66(156)$$
$$= 24(432) - 66[588 - 432(1)] \qquad \text{substitute for 156 using (1)}$$
$$= 588(-66) + 432(90)$$

Thus, $x = -66$ and $y = 90$.

Find integers x and y, if they exist, that satisfy the following equation.

1. $27x + 65y = 3$

2. $45x + 144y = 36$

3. $90x + 117y = 10$

4. $123x + 36y = 15$

5. $1032x + 1001y = 1$

6. $3125x + 3087y = 1$

NAME_____ DATE _____

Enrichment

Greatest Common Factor

Suppose we are given a linear equation $ax + by = c$ where a, b, and c are nonzero integers, and we want to know if there exist *integers x* and y that satisfy the equation. We could try guessing a few times, but this process would be time consuming for an equation such as $588x + 432y = 72$. By using the Euclidean Algorithm, we can determine not only if such integers x and y exist, but also find them. The following example shows how this algorithm works.

Example: Find integers x and y that satisfy $588x + 432y = 72$.

Divide the greater of the two coefficients by the lesser to get a quotient and remainder. Then, repeat the process by dividing the divisor by the remainder until you get a remainder of 0. The process can be written as follows.

$588 = 432(1) + 156$ (1)
$432 = 156(2) + 120$ (2)
$156 = 120(1) + 36$ (3)
$120 = 36(3) + 12$ (4)
 $36 = 12(3)$

The last nonzero remainder is the GCF of the two coefficients. If the constant term 72 is divisible by the GCF, then integers x and y do exist that satisfy the equation. To find x and y, work backward in the following manner.

$$
\begin{aligned}
72 &= 6 \cdot 12 \\
&= 6 \cdot [120 - 36(3)] && \text{substitute for 12 using (4)} \\
&= 6(120) - 18(36) \\
&= 6(120) - 18[156 - 120(1)] && \text{substitute for 36 using (3)} \\
&= -18(156) + 24(120) \\
&= -18(156) + 24[432 - 156(2)] && \text{substitute for 120 using (2)} \\
&= 24(432) - 66(156) \\
&= 24(432) - 66[588 - 432(1)] && \text{substitute for 156 using (1)} \\
&= 588(-66) + 432(90)
\end{aligned}
$$

Thus, $x = -66$ and $y = 90$.

Find integers x and y, if they exist, that satisfy the following equation.

1. $27x + 65y = 3$
    $x = -36$ and $y = 15$

2. $45x + 144y = 36$
    $x = -12$ and $y = 4$

3. $90x + 117y = 10$
    no integral solutions exist

4. $123x + 36y = 15$
    $x = 25$ and $y = -85$

5. $1032x + 1001y = 1$
    $x = -226$ and $y = 233$

6. $3125x + 3087y = 1$
    $x = -1381$ and $y = 1398$

            Algebra 2

Enrichment

Two-Intercept Form of a Linear Equation

Any linear equation that can be written in the form $\frac{x}{a} + \frac{y}{b} = 1$ has x-intercept a and y-intercept b.

Example: Draw the graph of $\frac{x}{-3} + \frac{y}{6} = 1$.

The graph crosses the x-axis at -3 and the y-axis at 6. Graph $(-3, 0)$ and $(0, 6)$, then draw a straight line through them.

Example: Write $3x + 4y = 12$ in two-intercept form.

Divide by 12 to obtain 1 on the right side. $\quad \frac{3x}{12} + \frac{4y}{12} = \frac{12}{12}$
Simplify.
The x-intercept is 4; the y-intercept is 3. $\quad \frac{x}{4} + \frac{y}{3} = 1$

Use the given intercepts a and b, to write an equation in two-intercept form. Then draw the graph.

1. $a = -2, b = -4$

2. $a = 1, b = 8$

3. $a = 3, b = 5$

4. $a = 6, b = 9$

Write each equation in two-intercept form. Then draw the graph.

5. $3x - 2y = -6$

6. $\frac{1}{2}x + \frac{1}{4}y = 1$

7. $5x + 2y = -10$

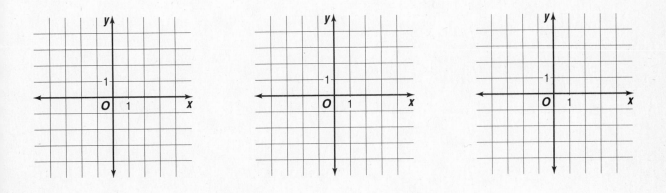

Two-Intercept Form of a Linear Equation

Any linear equation that can be written in the form $\frac{x}{a} + \frac{y}{b} = 1$ has x-intercept a and y-intercept b.

Example: Draw the graph of $\frac{x}{-3} + \frac{y}{6} = 1$.

The graph crosses the x-axis at -3 and the y-axis at 6. Graph $(-3, 0)$ and $(0, 6)$, then draw a straight line through them.

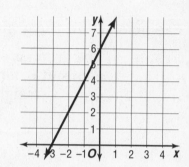

Example: Write $3x + 4y = 12$ in two-intercept form.

Divide by 12 to obtain 1 on the right side. $\quad \frac{3x}{12} + \frac{4y}{12} = \frac{12}{12}$
Simplify.
The x-intercept is 4; the y-intercept is 3. $\quad \frac{x}{4} + \frac{y}{3} = 1$

Use the given intercepts a and b, to write an equation in two-intercept form. Then draw the graph. See students' graphs.

1. $a = -2, b = -4$ $\quad \frac{x}{-2} + \frac{y}{-4} = 1$

2. $a = 1, b = 8$ $\quad \frac{x}{1} + \frac{y}{8} = 1$

3. $a = 3, b = 5$ $\quad \frac{x}{3} + \frac{y}{5} = 1$

4. $a = 6, b = 9$ $\quad \frac{x}{6} + \frac{y}{9} = 1$

Write each equation in two-intercept form. Then draw the graph.

5. $3x - 2y = -6$

$\frac{x}{-2} + \frac{y}{3} = 1$

6. $\frac{1}{2}x + \frac{1}{4}y = 1$

$\frac{x}{2} + \frac{y}{4} = 1$

7. $5x + 2y = -10$

$\frac{x}{-2} + \frac{y}{-5} = 1$

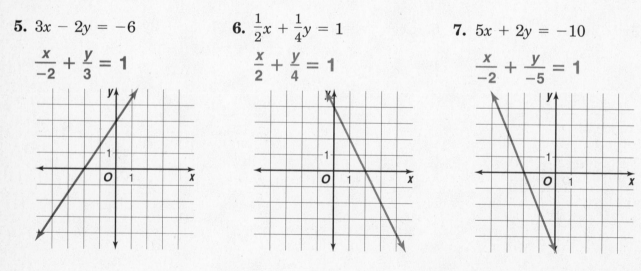

2-4

Enrichment

Finding Equations for Non-Linear Functions

You can often find an equation for a non-linear function by
looking for a pattern in a chart that shows values of the variables.

Example: Write an equation describing the relationship between
the variables in the chart.

	+1	+1	+1	+1	+1	+1

x	−3	−2	−1	0	1	2	3
y	2	1	0	1	2	3	4

	−1	−1	+1	+1	+1	+1

Notice that the function is not linear. The values of the y
are positive. As x goes from −3 to 3, the values of y decrease
steadily then increase steadily. This suggests a function similar
to $y = |x|$. Clearly $y = |x|$ does not quite work, but a little
adjustment shows that $y = |x + 1|$ does. Why is the equation
not $y = |x| + 1$?

Write an equation describing the relationship between the variables in each table.

1.

x	−3	−2	−1	0	1	2	3
y	4	3	2	1	0	1	2

2.

x	−3	−2	−1	0	1	2	3
y	6	4	2	0	2	4	6

3.

x	−3	−2	−1	0	1	2	3
y	8	5	2	1	4	7	10

Solve each of the following.

4. Rob's charges for mowing a lawn are directly proportional to
the number of hours he works. He charged Mr. Wilson $13.75
for 2.5 hours work. Write an equation for Rob's charges C as
a function of the number of hours h that he works.

5. A cube-shaped box with no top has a surface area of S square
units. Write an equation for the length E of an edge as a
function of S.

11

Enrichment

Finding Equations for Non-Linear Functions

You can often find an equation for a non-linear function by looking for a pattern in a chart that shows values of the variables.

Example: Write an equation describing the relationship between the variables in the chart.

+1   +1   +1 +1 +1 +1

x	−3	−2	−1	0	1	2	3
y	2	1	0	1	2	3	4

−1   −1   +1 +1 +1 +1

Notice that the function is not linear. The values of the y are positive. As x goes from −3 to 3, the values of y decrease steadily then increase steadily. This suggests a function similar to $y = |x|$. Clearly $y = |x|$ does not quite work, but a little adjustment shows that $y = |x + 1|$ does. Why is the equation not $y = |x| + 1$?
The y values would be 4, 3, 2, 1, 2, 3, 4.

Write an equation describing the relationship between the variables in each table.

1.

x	−3	−2	−1	0	1	2	3
y	4	3	2	1	0	1	2

$y = |x - 1|$

2.

x	−3	−2	−1	0	1	2	3
y	6	4	2	0	2	4	6

$y = |2x|$

3.

x	−3	−2	−1	0	1	2	3
y	8	5	2	1	4	7	10

$y = |3x + 1|$

Solve each of the following.

4. Rob's charges for mowing a lawn are directly proportional to the number of hours he works. He charged Mr. Wilson $13.75 for 2.5 hours work. Write an equation for Rob's charges C as a function of the number of hours h that he works.
$C = 5.5h$

5. A cube-shaped box with no top has a surface area of S square units. Write an equation for the length E of an edge as a function of S.
$E = \sqrt{\dfrac{S}{5}}$

Reading Mathematics

The following paragraph states a result you might be asked to prove in a mathematics course. Parts of the paragraph are numbered.

01 Let n be a positive integer.

02 Also, let $n_1 = s(n_1)$ be the sum of the squares of the digits in n.

03 Then $n_2 = s(n_1)$ is the sum of the squares of the digits of n_1, and $n_3 = s(n_2)$ is the sum of the squares of the digits of n_2.

04 In general, $n_k = s(n_{k-1})$ is the sum of the squares of the digits of n_{k-1}.

05 Consider the sequence: $n, n_1, n_2, n_3, \cdots, n_k, \cdots$.

06 In this sequence either all the terms from some k on have the value 1,

07 or some term, say n_j, has the value 4, so that the eight terms 4, 16, 37, 58, 89, 145, 42, and 20 keep repeating from that point on.

Use the paragraph to answer these questions.

1. Use the sentence in line 01. List the first five values of n.

2. Use 9246 for n and give an example to show the meaning of line 02.

3. In line 02, which symbol shows a function? Explain the function in a sentence.

4. For $n = 9246$, find n_2 and n_3 as described in sentence 03.

5. How do the first four sentences relate to sentence 05?

6. Use $n = 31$ and find the first four terms of the sequence.

7. Which sentence of the paragraph is illustrated by $n = 31$?

8. Use $n = 61$ and find the first ten terms.

9. Which sentence is illustrated by $n = 61$?

12

NAME_____ DATE _____

Enrichment

Reading Mathematics

The following paragraph states a result you might be asked to prove in a mathematics course. Parts of the paragraph are numbered.

01 Let n be a positive integer.

02 Also, let $n_1 = s(n_1)$ be the sum of the squares of the digits in n.

03 Then $n_2 = s(n_1)$ is the sum of the squares of the digits of n_1, and $n_3 = s(n_2)$ is the sum of the squares of the digits of n_2.

04 In general, $n_k = s(n_{k-1})$ is the sum of the squares of the digits of n_{k-1}.

05 Consider the sequence: $n, n_1, n_2, n_3, \cdots, n_k, \cdots$.

06 In this sequence either all the terms from some k on have the value 1,

07 or some term, say n_j, has the value 4, so that the eight terms 4, 16, 37, 58, 89, 145, 42, and 20 keep repeating from that point on.

Use the paragraph to answer these questions.

1. Use the sentence in line 01. List the first five values of n.
1, 2, 3, 4, 5

2. Use 9246 for n and give an example to show the meaning of line 02.
$n_1 = s(9246) = 137$, **because 137 = 81 + 4 + 16 + 36**

3. In line 02, which symbol shows a function? Explain the function in a sentence. $s(n)$; **the sum of the squares of the digits of a number is a function of the number**

4. For $n = 9246$, find n_2 and n_3 as described in sentence 03.
$n_2 = 59, n_3 = 106$

5. How do the first four sentences relate to sentence 05?
They explain how to compute the terms of the sequence.

6. Use $n = 31$ and find the first four terms of the sequence.
31, 10, 1, 1

7. Which sentence of the paragraph is illustrated by $n = 31$?
sentence 06

8. Use $n = 61$ and find the first ten terms.
61, 37, 58, 89, 145, 42, 20, 4, 16, 37

9. Which sentence is illustrated by $n = 61$?
sentence 07

2-6

Enrichment

Graphs of Functions that Use [x]

You may find it interesting to explore some of the unusual graphs that result by making use of the greatest integer function. When you graph these functions, use a colored pen or pencil. You will probably find it helpful to make a chart of values for each function.

Graph each function.

1. $y = 2x - [x]$

2. $y = \dfrac{[x]}{[x]}$

3. $y = \dfrac{[0.5x + 1]}{[0.5x + 1]}$

4. $y = \dfrac{x}{[x]}$

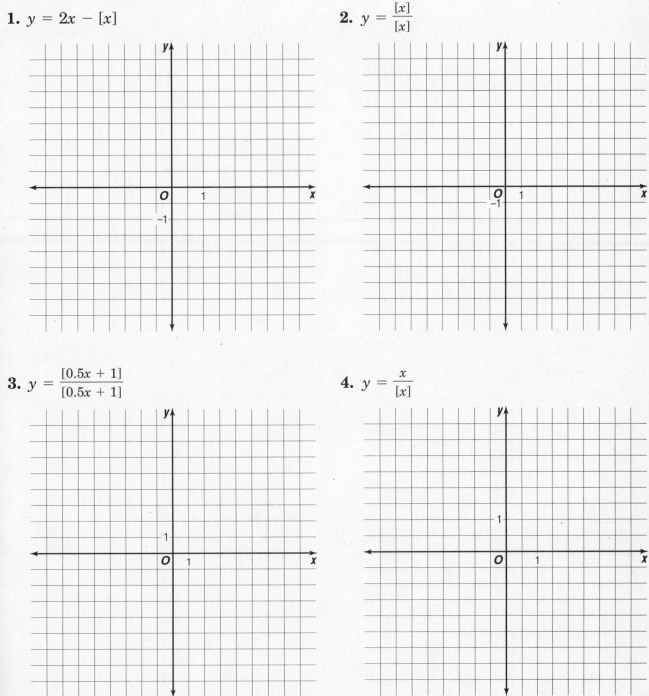

Enrichment

Graphs of Functions that Use [x]

You may find it interesting to explore some of the unusual
graphs that result by making use of the greatest integer
function. When you graph these functions, use a colored pen
or pencil. You will probably find it helpful to make a chart of
values for each function.

Graph each function.

1. $y = 2x - [x]$

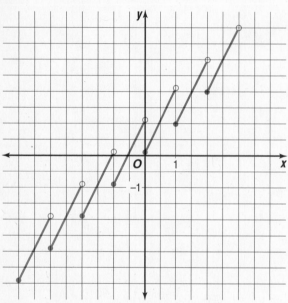

2. $y = \dfrac{[x]}{[x]}$

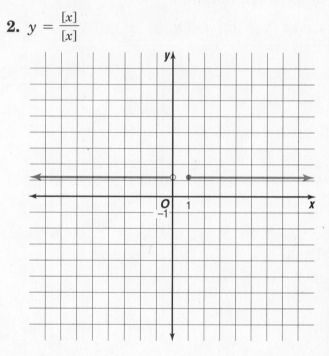

3. $y = \dfrac{[0.5x + 1]}{[0.5x + 1]}$

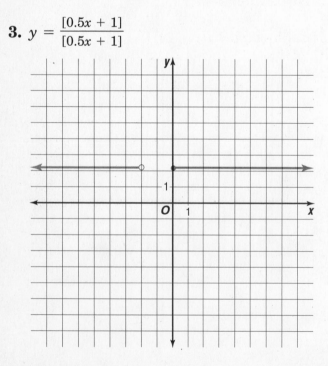

4. $y = \dfrac{x}{[x]}$

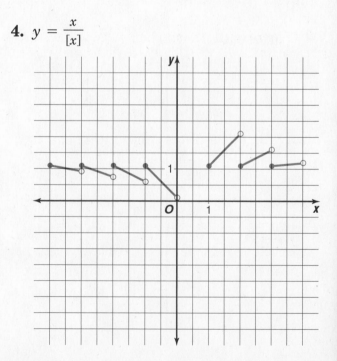

Algebra 2

2-7

Enrichment

Aerial Surveyors and Area

Many land regions have irregular shapes. Aerial surveyors often use coordinates when finding areas of such regions.

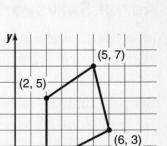

Step 1 List the ordered pairs for the vertices in counterclockwise order, repeating the first ordered pair at the bottom of the list.

Step 2 Find D, the sum of the downward diagonal products (from left to right).

$$D = (5 \cdot 5) + (2 \cdot 1) + (2 \cdot 3) + (6 \cdot 7)$$
$$= 25 + 2 + 6 + 42 \text{ or } 75$$

Step 3 Find U, the sum of the upward diagonal products (from left to right).

$$U = (2 \cdot 7) + (2 \cdot 5) + (6 \cdot 1) + (5 \cdot 3)$$
$$= 14 + 10 + 6 + 15 \text{ or } 45$$

$(5, 7)$

$(2, 5)$

$(2, 1)$

$(6, 3)$

$(5, 7)$

Step 4 Use the formula $A = \frac{1}{2}(D - U)$ to find the area.

$$A = \frac{1}{2}(75 - 45)$$
$$= \frac{1}{2}(30) \text{ or } 15$$

The area is 15 square units. Count the number of square units enclosed by the polygon. Does this result seem reasonable?

Use the coordinate method to find the area of each region in square units.

1.   **2.**   **3.**

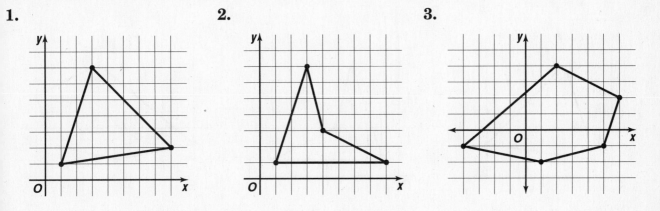

Enrichment

Aerial Surveyors and Area

Many land regions have irregular shapes. Aerial surveyors often use coordinates when finding areas of such regions.

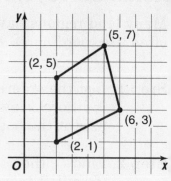

Step 1 List the ordered pairs for the vertices in counterclockwise order, repeating the first ordered pair at the bottom of the list.

Step 2 Find D, the sum of the downward diagonal products (from left to right).

$D = (5 \cdot 5) + (2 \cdot 1) + (2 \cdot 3) + (6 \cdot 7)$
$\quad = 25 + 2 + 6 + 42 \text{ or } 75$

Step 3 Find U, the sum of the upward diagonal products (from left to right).

$U = (2 \cdot 7) + (2 \cdot 5) + (6 \cdot 1) + (5 \cdot 3)$
$\quad = 14 + 10 + 6 + 15 \text{ or } 45$

Step 4 Use the formula $A = \frac{1}{2}(D - U)$ to find the area.

$A = \frac{1}{2}(75 - 45)$

$\quad = \frac{1}{2}(30) \text{ or } 15$

The area is 15 square units. Count the number of square units enclosed by the polygon. Does this result seem reasonable?

Use the coordinate method to find the area of each region in square units.

1. **2.** **3.**

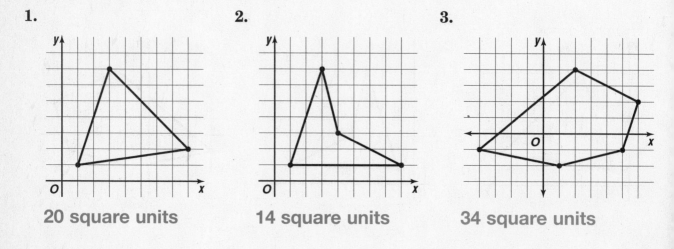

20 square units   14 square units   34 square units

Investments

The following graph represents two different investments. Line A represents an initial investment of $30,000 with a bank paying passbook savings interest. Line B represents an initial investment of $5,000 with a profitable mutual fund with dividends reinvested and capital gains accepted in shares. By deriving the linear equation $y = mx + b$ for A and B, a projection of the future can be made.

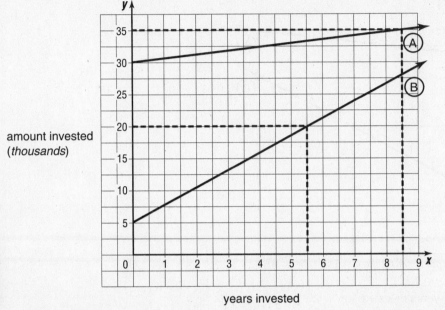

1. The y-intercept, b, is the initial investment. Find b for each of the following.
   a. line A   **b.** line B

2. The slope of the line, m, is the rate of return. Find m for each of the following.
   a. line A   **b.** line B

3. What are the equations of each of the following lines?
   a. line A   **b.** line B

4. What will be the value of the mutual fund after 11 years of investment?

5. What will be the value of the bank account after 11 years of investment?

6. When will the mutual fund and the bank account have equal value?

7. Which investment has the greatest payoff?

Enrichment

Investments

The following graph represents two different investments. Line A represents an initial investment of $30,000 with a bank paying passbook savings interest. Line B represents an initial investment of $5,000 with a profitable mutual fund with dividends reinvested and capital gains accepted in shares. By deriving the linear equation $y = mx + b$ for A and B, a projection of the future can be made.

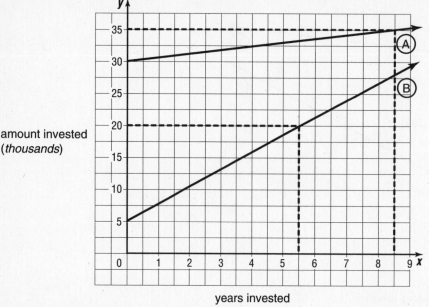

1. The y-intercept, b, is the initial investment. Find b for each of the following.
   a. line A **30,000**
   b. line B **5000**

2. The slope of the line, m, is the rate of return. Find m for each of the following.
   a. line A **0.588**
   b. line B **2.73**

3. What are the equations of each of the following lines?
   a. line A **$y = 0.588x + 30$**
   b. line B **$y = 2.73x + 5$**

4. What will be the value of the mutual fund after 11 years of investment?
   $35,030

5. What will be the value of the bank account after 11 years of investment?
   $36,468

6. When will the mutual fund and the bank account have equal value?
   after 11.67 years of investment

7. Which investment has the greatest payoff?
   the mutual fund

3-2

Enrichment

Using Coordinates

From one observation point, the line of sight to a downed plane is given by $y = x - 1$. From another observation point, the line of sight is given by $x + 3y = 21$. What are the coordinates of the point at which the crash occurred?

Solve the system of equations $\begin{cases} y = x - 1 \\ x + 3y = 21 \end{cases}$

$$x + 3y = 21$$
$$x + 3(x - 1) = 21 \qquad \textbf{Substitute } x - 1 \textbf{ for } y.$$
$$x + 3x - 3 = 21$$
$$4x = 24$$
$$x = 6$$

$$x + 3y = 21$$
$$6 + 3y = 21 \qquad \textbf{Substitute 6 for } x.$$
$$3y = 15$$
$$y = 5$$

The coordinates of the crash are (6, 5).

Solve the following.

1. The lines of sight to a forest fire are as follows.

   From Ranger Station A: $3x + y = 9$
   From Ranger Station B: $2x + 3y = 13$
   Find the coordinates of the fire.

2. A Delta flight is traveling along the line $x - y = -1$
   A TWA flight is traveling along the line $5x + 3y = 19$.
   If they continue along the same lines, at what point will the flight paths cross?

3. Two mine shafts are dug along the paths of the following equations.

   $$x - y = 1400$$
   $$2x + y = 1300$$

   If the shafts meet at a depth of 200 feet, what are the coordinates of the point at which they meet?

Enrichment

Using Coordinates

From one observation point, the line of sight to a downed plane is given by $y = x - 1$. From another observation point, the line of sight is given by $x + 3y = 21$. What are the coordinates of the point at which the crash occurred?

Solve the system of equations $\begin{cases} y = x - 1 \\ x + 3y = 21 \end{cases}$

$$x + 3y = 21$$
$$x + 3(x - 1) = 21 \qquad \text{Substitute } x - 1 \text{ for } y.$$
$$x + 3x - 3 = 21$$
$$4x = 24$$
$$x = 6$$

$$x + 3y = 21$$
$$6 + 3y = 21 \qquad \text{Substitute 6 for } x.$$
$$3y = 15$$
$$y = 5$$

The coordinates of the crash are $(6, 5)$.

Solve the following.

1. The lines of sight to a forest fire are as follows.

   From Ranger Station A: $3x + y = 9$
   From Ranger Station B: $2x + 3y = 13$
   Find the coordinates of the fire.
   (2, 3)

2. A Delta flight is traveling along the line $x - y = -1$
   A TWA flight is traveling along the line $5x + 3y = 19$.
   If they continue along the same lines, at what point will the flight paths cross?
   (2, 3)

3. Two mine shafts are dug along the paths of the following equations.

   $x - y = 1400$
   $2x + y = 1300$

   If the shafts meet at a depth of 200 feet, what are the coordinates of the point at which they meet?
   (900, −500)

Enrichment

Properties of Determinants

The following properties often help when evaluating determinants.

(1) If all the elements of a row (or column) are zero, the value of the determinant is zero.

$$\begin{vmatrix} a & b \\ 0 & 0 \end{vmatrix} = 0$$

(2) Multiplying all the elements of a row (or column) by a constant is equivalent to multiplying the value of the determinant by the constant.

$$3\begin{vmatrix} 4 & -1 \\ 5 & 3 \end{vmatrix} = \begin{vmatrix} 12 & -3 \\ 5 & 3 \end{vmatrix}$$

(3) If two rows (or columns) have equal corresponding elements, the value of the determinant is zero.

$$\begin{vmatrix} 5 & 5 \\ -3 & -3 \end{vmatrix} = 0$$

(4) The value of a determinant is unchanged if any multiple of a row (or column) is added to corresponding elements of another row (or column).

(Row 2 is added to row 1.) $\quad \begin{vmatrix} 4 & -3 \\ 2 & 5 \end{vmatrix} = \begin{vmatrix} 6 & 2 \\ 2 & 5 \end{vmatrix}$

(5) If two rows (or columns) are interchanged, the sign of the determinant is changed.

$$\begin{vmatrix} 4 & 5 \\ -3 & 8 \end{vmatrix} = -\begin{vmatrix} -3 & 8 \\ 4 & 5 \end{vmatrix}$$

(6) The value of the determinant is unchanged if row 1 is interchanged with column 1, and row 2 is interchanged with column 2. The result is called the transpose.

$$\begin{vmatrix} 5 & -7 \\ 3 & 4 \end{vmatrix} = \begin{vmatrix} 5 & 3 \\ -7 & 4 \end{vmatrix}$$

Exercises 1–6

Verify each property above by evaluating the given determinants and give another example of the property.

Enrichment

Properties of Determinants

The following properties often help when evaluating determinants.

(1) If all the elements of a row (or column) are zero, the value of the determinant is zero.

$$\begin{vmatrix} a & b \\ 0 & 0 \end{vmatrix} = 0 \qquad (a \cdot 0) - (0 \cdot b) = 0$$

(2) Multiplying all the elements of a row (or column) by a constant is equivalent to multiplying the value of the determinant by the constant.

$$3\begin{vmatrix} 4 & -1 \\ 5 & 3 \end{vmatrix} = \begin{vmatrix} 12 & -3 \\ 5 & 3 \end{vmatrix} \qquad \begin{aligned} 3[4(3) - 5(-1)] = \\ 3[12 + 5] = 51 \\ 12(3) - 5(-3) = 51 \end{aligned}$$

(3) If two rows (or columns) have equal corresponding elements, the value of the determinant is zero.

$$\begin{vmatrix} 5 & 5 \\ -3 & -3 \end{vmatrix} = 0 \qquad 5(-3) - (-3)(5) = 0$$

(4) The value of a determinant is unchanged if any multiple of a row (or column) is added to corresponding elements of another row (or column).

(Row 2 is added to row 1.)
$$\begin{vmatrix} 4 & -3 \\ 2 & 5 \end{vmatrix} = \begin{vmatrix} 6 & 2 \\ 2 & 5 \end{vmatrix}$$

$$\begin{aligned} 4(5) - 2(-3) = \\ 20 + 6 = 26 \end{aligned} \qquad \begin{aligned} 6(5) - 2(2) = \\ 30 - 4 = 26 \end{aligned}$$

(5) If two rows (or columns) are interchanged, the sign of the determinant is changed.

$$\begin{vmatrix} 4 & 5 \\ -3 & 8 \end{vmatrix} = -\begin{vmatrix} -3 & 8 \\ 4 & 5 \end{vmatrix}$$

$$\begin{aligned} 4(8) - (-3)(5) = \\ 32 + 15 = 47 \end{aligned} \qquad \begin{aligned} -[(-3)(5) - 4(8)] = \\ -[-15 - 32] = 47 \end{aligned}$$

(6) The value of the determinant is unchanged if row 1 is interchanged with column 1, and row 2 is interchanged with column 2. The result is called the transpose.

$$\begin{vmatrix} 5 & -7 \\ 3 & 4 \end{vmatrix} = \begin{vmatrix} 5 & 3 \\ -7 & 4 \end{vmatrix}$$

$$\begin{aligned} 5(4) - 3(-7) = \\ 20 + 21 = 41 \end{aligned} \qquad \begin{aligned} 5(4) - (-7)(3) = \\ 20 + 21 = 41 \end{aligned}$$

Exercises 1–6

Verify each property above by evaluating the given determinants and give another example of the property. **Examples will vary.**

Enrichment

Tracing Strategy

Try to trace over each of the figures below without tracing the
same segment twice.

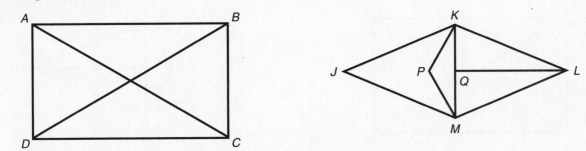

The figure at the left cannot be traced, but the one at the right
can. The rule is that a figure is traceable if it has no more than
two points where an odd number of segments meet. The figure
at the left has three segments meeting at each of the four
corners. However, the figure at the right has only two points,
L and Q, where an odd number of segments meet.

**Determine if each figure can be traced without tracing the
same segment twice. If it can, then name the starting point
and name the segments in the order they should be traced.**

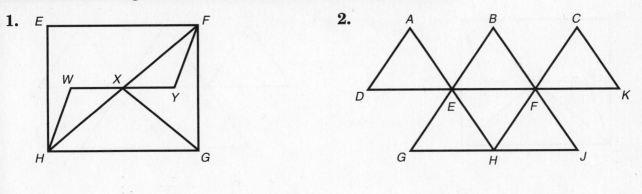

1.

2.

3.

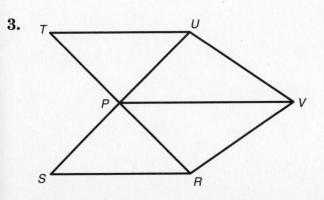

Enrichment

Tracing Strategy

Try to trace over each of the figures below without tracing the same segment twice.

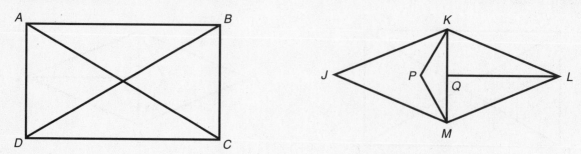

The figure at the left cannot be traced, but the one at the right can. The rule is that a figure is traceable if it has no more than two points where an odd number of segments meet. The figure at the left has three segments meeting at each of the four corners. However, the figure at the right has only two points, L and Q, where an odd number of segments meet.

Determine if each figure can be traced without tracing the same segment twice. If it can, then name the starting point and name the segments in the order they should be traced.

1.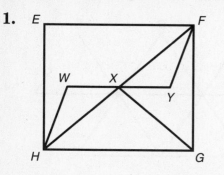

yes; X; $\overline{XY}$, $\overline{YF}$, $\overline{FX}$, $\overline{XG}$, $\overline{GF}$, $\overline{FE}$, $\overline{EH}$, $\overline{HX}$, $\overline{XW}$, $\overline{WH}$, $\overline{HG}$

2.

yes; E; $\overline{ED}$, $\overline{DA}$, $\overline{AE}$, $\overline{EB}$, $\overline{BF}$, $\overline{FC}$, $\overline{CK}$, $\overline{KF}$, $\overline{FJ}$, $\overline{JH}$, $\overline{HF}$, $\overline{FE}$, $\overline{EH}$, $\overline{AG}$, $\overline{GE}$

3.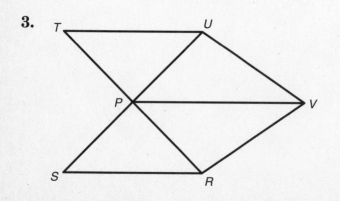

3-5

Enrichment

Truth Tables

In mathematics, the basic operations are addition, subtraction, multiplication, division, finding a root, and raising to a power. In logic, the basic operations are the following: *not* ($\sim$), *and* ($\wedge$), *or* ($\vee$), and *implies* ($\rightarrow$).

If P and Q are statements, then $\sim P$ means not P; $\sim Q$ means not Q; $P \wedge Q$ means P and Q; $P \vee Q$ means P or Q; and $P \rightarrow Q$ means P implies Q. The operations are defined by truth tables. On the left below is the truth table for the statement $\sim P$. Notice that there are two possible conditions for P, true (T) or false (F). If P is true, $\sim P$ is false; if P is false, $\sim P$ is true. Also shown are the truth tables for $P \wedge Q$, $P \vee Q$, and $P \rightarrow Q$.

P	$\sim P$
T	F
F	T

P	Q	$P \wedge Q$
T	T	T
T	F	F
F	T	F
F	F	F

P	Q	$P \vee Q$
T	T	T
T	F	T
F	T	T
F	F	F

P	Q	$P \rightarrow Q$
T	T	T
T	F	F
F	T	T
F	F	T

You can use this information to find out under what conditions a complex statement is true.

Example: Under what conditions is $\sim P \vee Q$ true?

Create the truth table for the statement. Use the information from the truth table above for $P \vee Q$ to complete the last column.

P	Q	$\sim P$	$\sim P \vee Q$
T	T	F	T
T	F	F	F
F	T	T	T
F	F	T	T

The truth table indicates that $\sim P \vee Q$ is true in all cases except where P is true and Q is false.

Use truth tables to determine the conditions under which each statement is true.

1. $\sim P \vee \sim Q$

2. $\sim P \rightarrow (P \rightarrow Q)$

3. $(P \vee Q) \vee (\sim P \wedge \sim Q)$

4. $(P \rightarrow Q) \vee (Q \rightarrow P)$

5. $(P \rightarrow Q) \wedge (Q \rightarrow P)$

6. $(\sim P \wedge \sim Q) \rightarrow \sim (P \vee Q)$

19

Enrichment

Truth Tables

In mathematics, the basic operations are addition, subtraction, multiplication, division, finding a root, and raising to a power. In logic, the basic operations are the following: *not* ($\sim$), *and* ($\wedge$), *or* ($\vee$), and *implies* ($\rightarrow$).

If P and Q are statements, then $\sim P$ means not P; $\sim Q$ means not Q; $P \wedge Q$ means P and Q; $P \vee Q$ means P or Q; and $P \rightarrow Q$ means P implies Q. The operations are defined by truth tables. On the left below is the truth table for the statement $\sim P$. Notice that there are two possible conditions for P, true (T) or false (F). If P is true, $\sim P$ is false; if P is false, $\sim P$ is true. Also shown are the truth tables for $P \wedge Q$, $P \vee Q$, and $P \rightarrow Q$.

P	$\sim P$
T	F
F	T

P	Q	$P \wedge Q$
T	T	T
T	F	F
F	T	F
F	F	F

P	Q	$P \vee Q$
T	T	T
T	F	T
F	T	T
F	F	F

P	Q	$P \rightarrow Q$
T	T	T
T	F	F
F	T	T
F	F	T

You can use this information to find out under what conditions a complex statement is true.

Example: Under what conditions is $\sim P \vee Q$ true?

Create the truth table for the statement. Use the information from the truth table above for $P \vee Q$ to complete the last column.

P	Q	$\sim P$	$\sim P \vee Q$
T	T	F	T
T	F	F	F
F	T	T	T
F	F	T	T

When one statement is true and one is false, the conjunction is true.

The truth table indicates that $\sim P \vee Q$ is true in all cases except where P is true and Q is false.

Use truth tables to determine the conditions under which each statement is true.

1. $\sim P \vee \sim Q$ **all except where both P and Q are true**

2. $\sim P \rightarrow (P \rightarrow Q)$ **all**

3. $(P \vee Q) \vee (\sim P \wedge \sim Q)$ **all**

4. $(P \rightarrow Q) \vee (Q \rightarrow P)$ **all**

5. $(P \rightarrow Q) \wedge (Q \rightarrow P)$ **both P and Q are true; both P and Q are false**

6. $(\sim P \wedge \sim Q) \rightarrow \sim (P \vee Q)$ **all**

Enrichment

Computer Circuits and Logic

Computers operate according to the laws of logic. The circuits of
a computer can be described using logic.

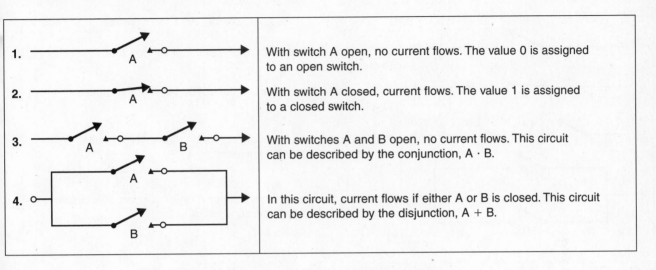

1. With switch A open, no current flows. The value 0 is assigned to an open switch.

2. With switch A closed, current flows. The value 1 is assigned to a closed switch.

3. With switches A and B open, no current flows. This circuit can be described by the conjunction, $A \cdot B$.

4. In this circuit, current flows if either A or B is closed. This circuit can be described by the disjunction, $A + B$.

A	B	A + B
0	0	0
0	1	1
1	0	1
1	1	1

Truth tables can be used to describe the
flow of current in a circuit. The table at
the left describes the circuit in diagram 4.
According to the table, the only time
current does not flow through the circuit
is when both switches A and B are open.

Draw a circuit diagram for each of the following.

1. $(A \cdot B) + C$

2. $(A + B) \cdot C$

3. $(A + B) \cdot (C + D)$

4. $(A \cdot B) + (C \cdot D)$

5. Construct a truth table for the
following circuit.

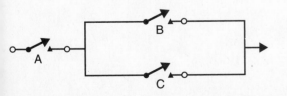

Enrichment

Computer Circuits and Logic

Computers operate according to the laws of logic. The circuits of a computer can be described using logic.

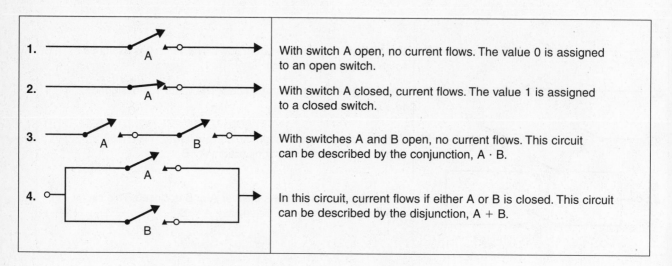

1. With switch A open, no current flows. The value 0 is assigned to an open switch.

2. With switch A closed, current flows. The value 1 is assigned to a closed switch.

3. With switches A and B open, no current flows. This circuit can be described by the conjunction, A · B.

4. In this circuit, current flows if either A or B is closed. This circuit can be described by the disjunction, A + B.

A	B	A + B
0	0	0
0	1	1
1	0	1
1	1	1

Truth tables can be used to describe the flow of current in a circuit. The table at the left describes the circuit in diagram 4. According to the table, the only time current does not flow through the circuit is when both switches A and B are open.

Draw a circuit diagram for each of the following.

1. (A · B) + C

2. (A + B) · C

3. (A + B) · (C + D)

4. (A · B) + (C · D)

5. Construct a truth table for the following circuit.

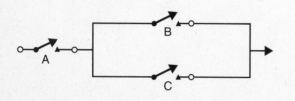

A	B	C	(B + C)	A(B + C)
0	0	0	0	0
0	0	1	1	0
0	1	1	1	0
0	1	0	1	0
1	0	1	1	1
1	1	0	1	1
1	1	1	1	1
1	0	0	0	0

Algebra 2

Enrichment

Billiards

The figure at the right shows a billiard table.
The object is to use a cue stick to strike the
ball at point C so that the ball will hit the
sides (or cushions) of the table at least once
before hitting the ball located at point A. In
playing the game, you need to locate point P.

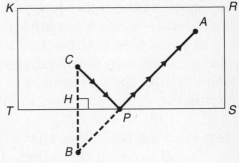

Step 1 Find point B so that $\overline{BC} \perp \overline{ST}$ and $\overline{BH} \cong \overline{CH}$.
B is called the reflected image of C in $\overline{ST}$.

Step 2 Draw $\overline{AB}$.

Step 3 $\overline{AB}$ intersects $\overline{ST}$ at the desired point P.

**For each billiards problem, the cue ball at point C must strike
the indicated cushion(s) and then strike the ball at point A.
Draw and label the correct path for the cue ball using the
process described above.**

1. cushion $\overline{KR}$

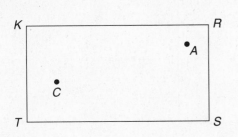

2. cushion $\overline{RS}$

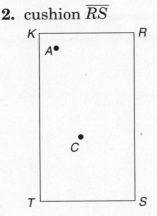

3. cushion $\overline{TS}$, then cushion $\overline{RS}$

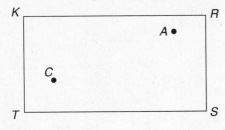

4. cushion $\overline{KT}$, then cushion $\overline{RS}$

NAME_____ DATE_____

Enrichment

Billiards

The figure at the right shows a billiard table. The object is to use a cue stick to strike the ball at point C so that the ball will hit the sides (or cushions) of the table at least once before hitting the ball located at point A. In playing the game, you need to locate point P.

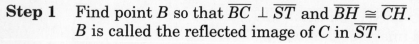

Step 1 Find point B so that $\overline{BC} \perp \overline{ST}$ and $\overline{BH} \cong \overline{CH}$. B is called the reflected image of C in $\overline{ST}$.

Step 2 Draw $\overline{AB}$.

Step 3 $\overline{AB}$ intersects $\overline{ST}$ at the desired point P.

For each billiards problem, the cue ball at point C must strike the indicated cushion(s) and then strike the ball at point A. Draw and label the correct path for the cue ball using the process described above.

1. cushion $\overline{KR}$

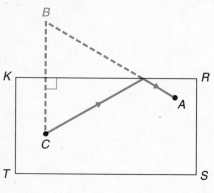

2. cushion $\overline{RS}$

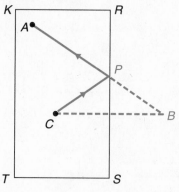

3. cushion $\overline{TS}$, then cushion $\overline{RS}$

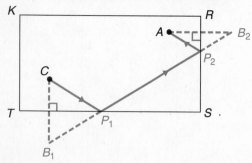

4. cushion $\overline{KT}$, then cushion $\overline{RS}$

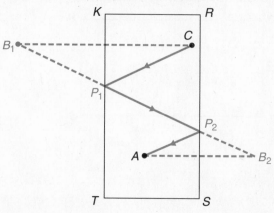

Enrichment

Tessellations

A tessellation is an arangement of polygons covering a plane without any gaps or overlapping. One example of a tessellation is a honeycomb. Three congruent regular hexagons meet at each vertex, and there is no wasted space between cells. This tessellation is called a regular tessellation since it is formed by congruent regular polygons.

A **semi-regular tessellation** is a tessellation formed by two or more regular polygons such that the number of sides of the polygons meeting at each vertex is the same.

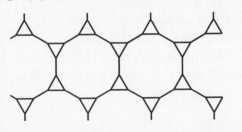

For example, the tessellation at the left has two regular dodecagons and one equilateral triangle meeting at each vertex. We can name this tessellation a 3-12-12 for the number of sides of each polygon that meet at one vertex.

Name each semi-regular tessellation shown according to the number of sides of the polygons that meet at each vertex.

1.

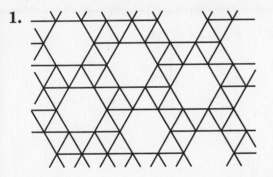

2.

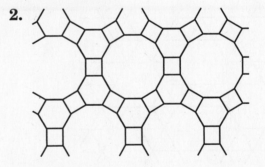

An equilateral triangle, two squares, and a regular hexagon can be used to surround a point in two different orders. Continue each pattern to see which is a semi-regular tessellation.

3. 3-4-4-6

4. 3-4-6-4

On another sheet of paper, draw part of each design. Then determine if it is a semi-regular tessellation.

5. 3-3-4-12   **6.** 3-4-3-12   **7.** 4-8-8   **8.** 3-3-3-4-4

NAME_____ DATE _____

Enrichment

Tessellations

A tessellation is an arangement of polygons covering a plane
without any gaps or overlapping. One example of a tessellation
is a honeycomb. Three congruent regular hexagons meet at
each vertex, and there is no wasted space between cells. This
tessellation is called a regular tessellation since it is formed
by congruent regular polygons.

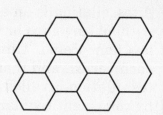

A **semi-regular tessellation** is a tessellation formed by two or
more regular polygons such that the number of sides of the
polygons meeting at each vertex is the same.

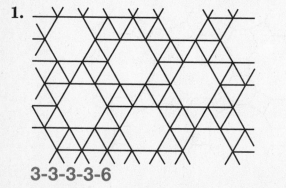

For example, the tessellation at the left has two
regular dodecagons and one equilateral triangle
meeting at each vertex. We can name this tessellation
a 3-12-12 for the number of sides of each polygon that
meet at one vertex.

**Name each semi-regular tessellation shown according to the
number of sides of the polygons that meet at each vertex.**

1.

3-3-3-3-6

2.

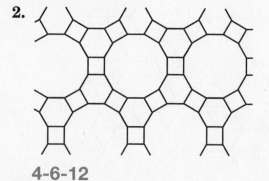

4-6-12

**An equilateral triangle, two squares, and a regular hexagon can
be used to surround a point in two different orders. Continue
each pattern to see which is a semi-regular tessellation.**

3. 3-4-4-6

not semi-regular

4. 3-4-6-4

semi-regular

**On another sheet of paper, draw part of each design. Then
determine if it is a semi-regular tessellation.**

5. 3-3-4-12
not semi-regular

6. 3-4-3-12
not semi-regular

7. 4-8-8
semi-regular

8. 3-3-3-4-4
semi-regular

Algebra 2

Enrichment

Sundaram's Sieve

The properties and patterns of prime numbers have fascinated many mathematicians. In 1934, a young East Indian student named Sundaram constructed the following matrix.

4	7	10	13	16	19	22	25	. . .
7	12	17	22	27	32	37	42	. . .
10	17	24	31	38	45	52	59	. . .
13	22	31	40	49	58	67	76	. . .
16	27	38	49	60	71	82	93	. . .

A surprising property of this matrix is that it can be used to determine whether or not some numbers are prime.

Complete these problems to discover this property.

1. The first row and the first column are created by using an arithmetic sequence. What is the common difference used in the sequence?

2. Find the next four numbers in the first row.

3. What are the common differences used to create the sequences in rows 2, 3, 4, and 5?

4. Write the next two rows of the matrix. Include eight numbers in each row.

5. Choose any five numbers from the matrix. For each number n, that you chose from the matrix, find $2n + 1$.

6. Write the factorization of each value of $2n + 1$ that you found in problem 5.

7. Use your results from problems 5 and 6 to complete this statement: If n occurs in the matrix, then $2n + 1$ _____ (is/is not) a prime number.

8. Choose any five numbers that are not in the matrix. Find $2n + 1$ for each of these numbers. Show that each result is a prime number.

9. Complete this statement: If n does not occur in the matrix, then $2n + 1$ is _____.

Enrichment

Sundaram's Sieve

The properties and patterns of prime numbers have fascinated many mathematicians. In 1934, a young East Indian student named Sundaram constructed the following matrix.

4	7	10	13	16	19	22	25	. . .
7	12	17	22	27	32	37	42	. . .
10	17	24	31	38	45	52	59	. . .
13	22	31	40	49	58	67	76	. . .
16	27	38	49	60	71	82	93	. . .

. . . .

A surprising property of this matrix is that it can be used to determine whether or not some numbers are prime.

Complete these problems to discover this property.

1. The first row and the first column are created by using an arithmetic sequence. What is the common difference used in the sequence?
   3

2. Find the next four numbers in the first row.
   28, 31, 34, 37

3. What are the common differences used to create the sequences in rows 2, 3, 4, and 5?
   5, 7, 9, 11

4. Write the next two rows of the matrix. Include eight numbers in each row. **row 6: 19, 32, 45, 58, 71, 84, 97, 110**
   row 7: 22, 37, 52, 67, 82, 97, 112, 127

5. Choose any five numbers from the matrix. For each number n, that you chose from the matrix, find $2n + 1$.
   Answers will vary.

6. Write the factorization of each value of $2n + 1$ that you found in problem 5. **Answers will vary, but all numbers are composite.**

7. Use your results from problems 5 and 6 to complete this statement: If n occurs in the matrix, then $2n + 1$ **is not** (is/is not) a prime number.

8. Choose any five numbers that are not in the matrix. Find $2n + 1$ for each of these numbers. Show that each result is a prime number.
   Answers will vary, but all numbers are prime.

9. Complete this statement: If n does not occur in the matrix, then $2n + 1$ is **a prime number**.

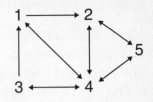
Enrichment

Student Edition
Pages 199–204

Communications Networks

The diagram at the right represents a communications network linking five computer remote stations. The arrows indicate the direction in which signals can be transmitted and received by each computer. We can generate a matrix to describe this network.

$$A = \begin{bmatrix} 0 & 1 & 0 & 1 & 0 \\ 0 & 0 & 0 & 1 & 1 \\ 1 & 0 & 0 & 1 & 0 \\ 1 & 1 & 1 & 0 & 1 \\ 0 & 1 & 0 & 1 & 0 \end{bmatrix}$$

The entry in position a_{ij} represents the number of ways to send a message from computer i to computer j directly. Compare the entries of matrix A to the diagram to verify the entries.

Matrix A is a communications network for direct communication. Suppose you want to send a message from one computer to another using exactly one other computer as a relay point. It can be shown that the entries of matrix A^2 represent the number of ways to send a message from one point to another using exactly one relay point.

$$A^2 = \begin{bmatrix} 1 & 1 & 1 & 1 & 2 \\ 1 & 2 & 1 & 1 & 1 \\ 1 & 2 & 1 & 1 & 1 \\ 1 & 2 & 0 & 4 & 1 \\ 1 & 1 & 1 & 1 & 2 \end{bmatrix}$$

Again, compare the entries of matrix A^2 to the communications diagram to verify that the entries are correct. Matrix A^2 represents using exactly one relay.

For each network, find the matrices A and A². Then write the number of ways the messages can be sent for each matrix.

1.
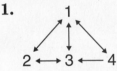

2.
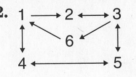

3.
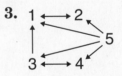

Algebra 2

NAME_____ DATE _____

Enrichment

Communications Networks

The diagram at the right represents a communications network linking five computer remote stations. The arrows indicate the direction in which signals can be transmitted and received by each computer. We can generate a matrix to describe this network.

$$A = \begin{bmatrix} 0 & 1 & 0 & 1 & 0 \\ 0 & 0 & 0 & 1 & 1 \\ 1 & 0 & 0 & 1 & 0 \\ 1 & 1 & 1 & 0 & 1 \\ 0 & 1 & 0 & 1 & 0 \end{bmatrix}$$

The entry in position a_{ij} represents the number of ways to send a message from computer i to computer j directly. Compare the entries of matrix A to the diagram to verify the entries.

Matrix A is a communications network for direct communication. Suppose you want to send a message from one computer to another using exactly one other computer as a relay point. It can be shown that the entries of matrix A^2 represent the number of ways to send a message from one point to another using exactly one relay point.

$$A^2 = \begin{bmatrix} 1 & 1 & 1 & 1 & 2 \\ 1 & 2 & 1 & 1 & 1 \\ 1 & 2 & 1 & 1 & 1 \\ 1 & 2 & 0 & 4 & 1 \\ 1 & 1 & 1 & 1 & 2 \end{bmatrix}$$

Again, compare the entries of matrix A^2 to the communications diagram to verify that the entries are correct. Matrix A^2 represents using exactly one relay.

For each network, find the matrices A and A². Then write the number of ways the messages can be sent for each matrix.

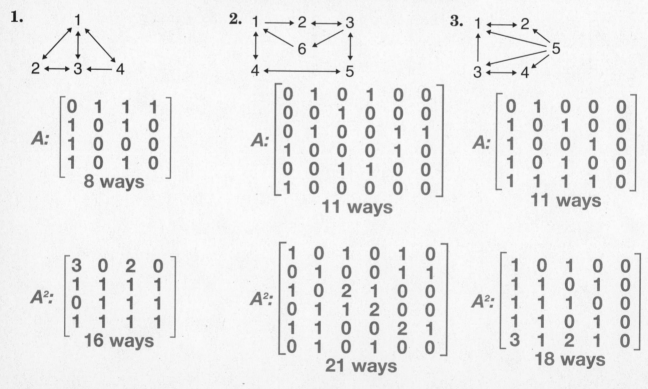

1.

A:
$$\begin{bmatrix} 0 & 1 & 1 & 1 \\ 1 & 0 & 1 & 0 \\ 1 & 0 & 0 & 0 \\ 1 & 0 & 1 & 0 \end{bmatrix}$$
8 ways

A^2:
$$\begin{bmatrix} 3 & 0 & 2 & 0 \\ 1 & 1 & 1 & 1 \\ 0 & 1 & 1 & 1 \\ 1 & 1 & 1 & 1 \end{bmatrix}$$
16 ways

2.

A:
$$\begin{bmatrix} 0 & 1 & 0 & 1 & 0 & 0 \\ 0 & 0 & 1 & 0 & 0 & 0 \\ 0 & 1 & 0 & 0 & 1 & 1 \\ 1 & 0 & 0 & 0 & 1 & 0 \\ 0 & 0 & 1 & 1 & 0 & 0 \\ 1 & 0 & 0 & 0 & 0 & 0 \end{bmatrix}$$
11 ways

A^2:
$$\begin{bmatrix} 1 & 0 & 1 & 0 & 1 & 0 \\ 0 & 1 & 0 & 0 & 1 & 1 \\ 1 & 0 & 2 & 1 & 0 & 0 \\ 0 & 1 & 1 & 2 & 0 & 0 \\ 1 & 1 & 0 & 0 & 2 & 1 \\ 0 & 1 & 0 & 1 & 0 & 0 \end{bmatrix}$$
21 ways

3.

A:
$$\begin{bmatrix} 0 & 1 & 0 & 0 & 0 \\ 1 & 0 & 1 & 0 & 0 \\ 1 & 0 & 0 & 1 & 0 \\ 1 & 0 & 1 & 0 & 0 \\ 1 & 1 & 1 & 1 & 0 \end{bmatrix}$$
11 ways

A^2:
$$\begin{bmatrix} 1 & 0 & 1 & 0 & 0 \\ 1 & 1 & 0 & 1 & 0 \\ 1 & 1 & 1 & 0 & 0 \\ 1 & 1 & 0 & 1 & 0 \\ 3 & 1 & 2 & 1 & 0 \end{bmatrix}$$
18 ways

4-4

Enrichment

Fourth-Order Determinants

Expansion by minors may be used to find the value of a 4×4 determinant, as shown below.

First write the expansion. Use the first row of the determinant. Remember that the signs of the terms alternate.

$$\begin{vmatrix} 6 & -3 & 2 & 7 \\ 0 & 4 & 3 & 5 \\ 0 & 2 & 1 & -4 \\ 6 & 0 & -2 & 0 \end{vmatrix} = 6\begin{vmatrix} 4 & 3 & 5 \\ 2 & 1 & -4 \\ 0 & -2 & 0 \end{vmatrix} - (-3)\begin{vmatrix} 0 & 3 & 5 \\ 0 & 1 & -4 \\ 6 & -2 & 0 \end{vmatrix} + 2\begin{vmatrix} 0 & 4 & 5 \\ 0 & 2 & -4 \\ 6 & 0 & 0 \end{vmatrix} - 7\begin{vmatrix} 0 & 4 & 3 \\ 0 & 2 & 1 \\ 6 & 0 & -2 \end{vmatrix}$$

Then evaluate each 3×3 determinant. Use any row.

$$\begin{vmatrix} 4 & 3 & 5 \\ 2 & 1 & -4 \\ 0 & -2 & 0 \end{vmatrix} = -(-2)\begin{vmatrix} 4 & 5 \\ 2 & -4 \end{vmatrix}$$
$$= 2(-16 - 10)$$
$$= -52$$

$$\begin{vmatrix} 0 & 3 & 5 \\ 0 & 1 & -4 \\ 6 & -2 & 0 \end{vmatrix} = -3\begin{vmatrix} 0 & -4 \\ 6 & 0 \end{vmatrix} + 5\begin{vmatrix} 0 & 1 \\ 6 & -2 \end{vmatrix}$$
$$= -3(24) + 5(-6)$$
$$= -102$$

$$\begin{vmatrix} 0 & 4 & 5 \\ 0 & 2 & -4 \\ 6 & 0 & 0 \end{vmatrix} = 6\begin{vmatrix} 4 & 5 \\ 2 & -4 \end{vmatrix}$$
$$= 6(-16 - 10)$$
$$= -156$$

$$\begin{vmatrix} 0 & 4 & 3 \\ 0 & 2 & 1 \\ 6 & 0 & -2 \end{vmatrix} = -4\begin{vmatrix} 0 & 1 \\ 6 & -2 \end{vmatrix} + 3\begin{vmatrix} 0 & 2 \\ 6 & 0 \end{vmatrix}$$
$$= -4(-6) + 3(-12)$$
$$= -12$$

Finally, evaluate the original 4×4 determinant.

$$\begin{vmatrix} 6 & -3 & 2 & 7 \\ 0 & 4 & 3 & 5 \\ 0 & 2 & 1 & -4 \\ 6 & 0 & -2 & 0 \end{vmatrix} = 6(-52) + 3(-102) + 2(-156) - 7(-12) = -846$$

Evaluate each determinant.

1. $\begin{vmatrix} 1 & 2 & 3 & 1 \\ 4 & 3 & -1 & 0 \\ 2 & -5 & 4 & 4 \\ 1 & -2 & 0 & 2 \end{vmatrix}$

2. $\begin{vmatrix} 3 & 3 & 3 & 3 \\ 2 & 1 & 2 & 1 \\ 4 & 3 & -1 & 5 \\ 2 & 5 & 0 & 1 \end{vmatrix}$

3. $\begin{vmatrix} 1 & 4 & 3 & 0 \\ -2 & -3 & 6 & 4 \\ 5 & 1 & 1 & 2 \\ 4 & 2 & 5 & -1 \end{vmatrix}$

Enrichment

Fourth-Order Determinants

Expansion by minors may be used to find the value of a 4 × 4 determinant, as shown below.

First write the expansion. Use the first row of the determinant. Remember that the signs of the terms alternate.

$$\begin{vmatrix} 6 & -3 & 2 & 7 \\ 0 & 4 & 3 & 5 \\ 0 & 2 & 1 & -4 \\ 6 & 0 & -2 & 0 \end{vmatrix} = 6\begin{vmatrix} 4 & 3 & 5 \\ 2 & 1 & -4 \\ 0 & -2 & 0 \end{vmatrix} - (-3)\begin{vmatrix} 0 & 3 & 5 \\ 0 & 1 & -4 \\ 6 & -2 & 0 \end{vmatrix} + 2\begin{vmatrix} 0 & 4 & 5 \\ 0 & 2 & -4 \\ 6 & 0 & 0 \end{vmatrix} - 7\begin{vmatrix} 0 & 4 & 3 \\ 0 & 2 & 1 \\ 6 & 0 & -2 \end{vmatrix}$$

Then evaluate each 3 × 3 determinant. Use any row.

$$\begin{vmatrix} 4 & 3 & 5 \\ 2 & 1 & -4 \\ 0 & -2 & 0 \end{vmatrix} = -(-2)\begin{vmatrix} 4 & 5 \\ 2 & -4 \end{vmatrix}$$
$$= 2(-16 - 10)$$
$$= -52$$

$$\begin{vmatrix} 0 & 3 & 5 \\ 0 & 1 & -4 \\ 6 & -2 & 0 \end{vmatrix} = -3\begin{vmatrix} 0 & -4 \\ 6 & 0 \end{vmatrix} + 5\begin{vmatrix} 0 & 1 \\ 6 & -2 \end{vmatrix}$$
$$= -3(24) + 5(-6)$$
$$= -102$$

$$\begin{vmatrix} 0 & 4 & 5 \\ 0 & 2 & -4 \\ 6 & 0 & 0 \end{vmatrix} = 6\begin{vmatrix} 4 & 5 \\ 2 & -4 \end{vmatrix}$$
$$= 6(-16 - 10)$$
$$= -156$$

$$\begin{vmatrix} 0 & 4 & 3 \\ 0 & 2 & 1 \\ 6 & 0 & -2 \end{vmatrix} = -4\begin{vmatrix} 0 & 1 \\ 6 & -2 \end{vmatrix} + 3\begin{vmatrix} 0 & 2 \\ 6 & 0 \end{vmatrix}$$
$$= -4(-6) + 3(-12)$$
$$= -12$$

Finally, evaluate the original 4 × 4 determinant.

$$\begin{vmatrix} 6 & -3 & 2 & 7 \\ 0 & 4 & 3 & 5 \\ 0 & 2 & 1 & -4 \\ 6 & 0 & -2 & 0 \end{vmatrix} = 6(-52) + 3(-102) + 2(-156) - 7(-12) = -846$$

Evaluate each determinant.

1. $\begin{vmatrix} 1 & 2 & 3 & 1 \\ 4 & 3 & -1 & 0 \\ 2 & -5 & 4 & 4 \\ 1 & -2 & 0 & 2 \end{vmatrix}$
−109

2. $\begin{vmatrix} 3 & 3 & 3 & 3 \\ 2 & 1 & 2 & 1 \\ 4 & 3 & -1 & 5 \\ 2 & 5 & 0 & 1 \end{vmatrix}$
−72

3. $\begin{vmatrix} 1 & 4 & 3 & 0 \\ -2 & -3 & 6 & 4 \\ 5 & 1 & 1 & 2 \\ 4 & 2 & 5 & -1 \end{vmatrix}$
−676

Algebra 2

Enrichment

Permutation Matrices

A permutation matrix is a square matrix in which each row and each column has one entry that is 1. All the other entries are 0. It is easy to find the inverse of a permutation matrix. You just interchange the rows and columns.

$$P = \begin{bmatrix} 0 & 0 & 1 & 0 \\ 0 & 1 & 0 & 0 \\ 0 & 0 & 0 & 1 \\ 1 & 0 & 0 & 0 \end{bmatrix} \qquad P^{-1} = \begin{bmatrix} 0 & 0 & 0 & 1 \\ 0 & 1 & 0 & 0 \\ 1 & 0 & 0 & 0 \\ 0 & 0 & 1 & 0 \end{bmatrix}$$

P is a 4×4 permutation matrix. P^{-1} is the inverse of P.

Solve each problem.

1. There is just one 2×2 permutation matrix that is not also an identity matrix. Write this matrix.

2. Find the inverse of the matrix you wrote in problem 1. What do you notice?

3. Show that the two matrices in problems 1 and 2 are inverses.

4. Write the inverse of this matrix. $B = \begin{bmatrix} 0 & 0 & 1 \\ 1 & 0 & 0 \\ 0 & 1 & 0 \end{bmatrix}$

5. Use B^{-1} from problem 4. Verify that B and B^{-1} are inverses.

6. Permutation matrices can be used to write and decipher codes. To see how this is done, use the message matrix M and matrix B from problem 4. Find matrix C so that C equals the product MB. Use the rules below.

   0 times a letter = 0
   1 times a letter = the same letter
   0 plus a letter = the same letter

   $M = \begin{bmatrix} S & H & E \\ S & A & W \\ H & I & M \end{bmatrix}$

7. Now find the product CB^{-1}. What do you notice?

NAME_____ DATE _____

Enrichment

Permutation Matrices

A permutation matrix is a square matrix in which each row and each column has one entry that is 1. All the other entries are 0. It is easy to find the inverse of a permutation matrix. You just interchange the rows and columns.

$$P = \begin{bmatrix} 0 & 0 & 1 & 0 \\ 0 & 1 & 0 & 0 \\ 0 & 0 & 0 & 1 \\ 1 & 0 & 0 & 0 \end{bmatrix} \quad P^{-1} = \begin{bmatrix} 0 & 0 & 0 & 1 \\ 0 & 1 & 0 & 0 \\ 1 & 0 & 0 & 0 \\ 0 & 0 & 1 & 0 \end{bmatrix}$$

P is a 4×4 permutation matrix. P^{-1} is the inverse of P.

Solve each problem.

1. There is just one 2×2 permutation matrix that is not also an identity matrix. Write this matrix.

$$\begin{bmatrix} 0 & 1 \\ 1 & 0 \end{bmatrix}$$

2. Find the inverse of the matrix you wrote in problem 1. What do you notice?

$$\begin{bmatrix} 0 & 1 \\ 1 & 0 \end{bmatrix}$$ The two matrices are the same.

3. Show that the two matrices in problems 1 and 2 are inverses.

$$\begin{bmatrix} 0\cdot1 + 1\cdot1 & 0\cdot1 + 1\cdot0 \\ 1\cdot0 + 0\cdot1 & 1\cdot1 + 0\cdot0 \end{bmatrix} = \begin{bmatrix} 1 & 0 \\ 0 & 1 \end{bmatrix}$$

4. Write the inverse of this matrix.

$$B = \begin{bmatrix} 0 & 0 & 1 \\ 1 & 0 & 0 \\ 0 & 1 & 0 \end{bmatrix}$$

$$B^{-1} = \begin{bmatrix} 0 & 1 & 0 \\ 0 & 0 & 1 \\ 1 & 0 & 0 \end{bmatrix}$$

5. Use B^{-1} from problem 4. Verify that B and B^{-1} are inverses.

$$\begin{bmatrix} 0\cdot0 + 0\cdot0 + 1\cdot1 & 0\cdot1 + 0\cdot0 + 1\cdot0 & 0\cdot0 + 0\cdot1 + 1\cdot0 \\ 1\cdot0 + 0\cdot0 + 0\cdot1 & 1\cdot1 + 0\cdot0 + 0\cdot0 & 1\cdot0 + 0\cdot1 + 0\cdot0 \\ 0\cdot0 + 1\cdot0 + 0\cdot1 & 0\cdot1 + 1\cdot0 + 0\cdot0 & 0\cdot0 + 1\cdot1 + 0\cdot0 \end{bmatrix} = \begin{bmatrix} 1 & 0 & 0 \\ 0 & 1 & 0 \\ 0 & 0 & 1 \end{bmatrix}$$

6. Permutation matrices can be used to write and decipher codes. To see how this is done, use the message matrix M and matrix B from problem 4. Find matrix C so that C equals the product MB. Use the rules below.

0 times a letter = 0
1 times a letter = the same letter
0 plus a letter = the same letter

$$M = \begin{bmatrix} S & H & E \\ S & A & W \\ H & I & M \end{bmatrix} \quad C = \begin{bmatrix} H & E & S \\ A & W & S \\ I & M & H \end{bmatrix}$$

7. Now find the product CB^{-1}. What do you notice?

$$\begin{bmatrix} H & E & S \\ A & W & S \\ I & M & H \end{bmatrix} \cdot \begin{bmatrix} 0 & 1 & 0 \\ 0 & 0 & 1 \\ 1 & 0 & 0 \end{bmatrix} = \begin{bmatrix} S & H & E \\ S & A & W \\ H & I & M \end{bmatrix}$$

Multiplying M by B encodes the message. To decipher, multiply by B^{-1}.

Enrichment

Properties of Matrices

Computing with matrices is different from computing with real numbers. Stated below are some properties of the real number system. Are these also true for matrices? In the problems on this page, you will investigate this question.

For all real numbers a and b, $ab = 0$ if and only if $a = 0$ or $b = 0$.

Multiplication is commutative. For all real numbers a and b, $ab = ba$.

Multiplication is associative. For all real numbers a, b, and c, $a(bc) = (ab)c$.

Use the matrices A, B, and C for the problems. Write whether each statement is true. Assume that a 2-by-2 matrix is the 0 matrix if and only if all of its elements are zero.

$$A = \begin{bmatrix} 3 & 1 \\ 1 & 3 \end{bmatrix} \qquad B = \begin{bmatrix} 1 & -3 \\ -1 & 3 \end{bmatrix} \qquad C = \begin{bmatrix} 3 & 6 \\ 1 & 2 \end{bmatrix}$$

1. $AB = 0$

2. $AC = 0$

3. $BC = 0$

4. $AB = BA$

5. $AC = CA$

6. $BC = CB$

7. $A(BC) = (AB)C$

8. $B(CA) = (BC)A$

9. $B(AC) = (BA)C$

10. Write a statement summarizing your findings about the properties of matrix multiplication.

Enrichment

Properties of Matrices

Computing with matrices is different from computing with real numbers. Stated below are some properties of the real number system. Are these also true for matrices? In the problems on this page, you will investigate this question.

For all real numbers a and b, $ab = 0$ if and only if $a = 0$ or $b = 0$.

Multiplication is commutative. For all real numbers a and b, $ab = ba$.

Multiplication is associative. For all real numbers a, b, and c, $a(bc) = (ab)c$.

Use the matrices A, B, and C for the problems. Write whether each statement is true. Assume that a 2-by-2 matrix is the 0 matrix if and only if all of its elements are zero.

$$A = \begin{bmatrix} 3 & 1 \\ 1 & 3 \end{bmatrix} \qquad B = \begin{bmatrix} 1 & -3 \\ -1 & 3 \end{bmatrix} \qquad C = \begin{bmatrix} 3 & 6 \\ 1 & 2 \end{bmatrix}$$

1. $AB = 0$ **no**

$$AB = \begin{bmatrix} 2 & -6 \\ -2 & 6 \end{bmatrix}$$

2. $AC = 0$ **no**

$$AC = \begin{bmatrix} 10 & 20 \\ 6 & 12 \end{bmatrix}$$

3. $BC = 0$ **yes**

$$BC = \begin{bmatrix} 0 & 0 \\ 0 & 0 \end{bmatrix}$$

4. $AB = BA$ **no**

$$BA = \begin{bmatrix} 0 & -8 \\ 0 & 8 \end{bmatrix}$$

So, $AB \neq BA$.

5. $AC = CA$ **no**

$$CA = \begin{bmatrix} 15 & 21 \\ 5 & 7 \end{bmatrix}$$

So, $AC \neq CA$.

6. $BC = CB$ **no**

$$CB = \begin{bmatrix} -3 & 9 \\ -1 & 3 \end{bmatrix}$$

So, $BC \neq CB$.

7. $A(BC) = (AB)C$ **yes**
Both products equal
$$\begin{bmatrix} 0 & 0 \\ 0 & 0 \end{bmatrix}.$$

8. $B(CA) = (BC)A$ **yes**
Both products equal
$$\begin{bmatrix} 0 & 0 \\ 0 & 0 \end{bmatrix}.$$

9. $B(AC) = (BA)C$ **yes**
Both products equal
$$\begin{bmatrix} -8 & -16 \\ 8 & 16 \end{bmatrix}.$$

10. Write a statement summarizing your findings about the properties of matrix multiplication.
Based on these examples, matrix multiplication is associative, but not commutative. Two matrices may have a product of zero even if neither of the factors equals zero.

4-7

Enrichment

Matrix Multiplication

A furniture manufacturer makes upholstered chairs and wood tables. Matrix A shows the number of hours spent on each item by three different workers. One day the factory receives an order for 10 chairs and 3 tables. This is shown in matrix B.

$$
\begin{array}{c}
\text{hours} \\
\begin{array}{ccc} \text{woodworker} & \text{finisher} & \text{upholsterer} \end{array}
\end{array}
$$

$$
\begin{array}{c} \text{chair} \\ \text{table} \end{array}
\begin{bmatrix} 4 & 2 & 12 \\ 18 & 15 & 0 \end{bmatrix} = A
\qquad
\begin{array}{c} \\ \text{number ordered} \end{array}
\begin{array}{cc} \text{chair} & \text{table} \end{array}
[\,10 \quad 3\,] = B
$$

$$
[10 \quad 3]\begin{bmatrix} 4 & 2 & 12 \\ 18 & 15 & 0 \end{bmatrix} = [10(4) + 3(18) \quad 10(2) + 3(15) \quad 10(12) + 3(0)] = [94 \quad 65 \quad 120]
$$

The product of the two matrices shows the number of hours needed for each type of worker to complete the order: 94 hours for woodworking, 65 hours for finishing, and 120 hours for upholstering.

To find the total labor cost, multiply by a matrix that shows the hourly rate for each worker: $15 for woodworking, $9 for finishing, and $12 for upholstering.

$$
C = \begin{bmatrix} 15 \\ 9 \\ 12 \end{bmatrix} \quad [94 \quad 65 \quad 120]\begin{bmatrix} 15 \\ 9 \\ 12 \end{bmatrix} = [94(15) + 65(9) + 120(12)] = \$3435
$$

Use matrix multiplication to solve this problem.

A candy company packages caramels, chocolates, and hard candy in three different assortments: traditional, deluxe, and superb. For each type of candy the table below gives the number in each assortment, the number of Calories per piece, and the cost to make each piece.

	traditional	deluxe	superb	Calories per piece	cost per piece in cents
caramels	10	16	15	60	10
chocolates	12	8	25	70	12
hard candy	10	16	8	55	6

The company receives an order for 300 traditional, 180 deluxe and 100 superb assortments.

1. Find the number of each type of candy needed to fill the order.

2. Find the total number of Calories in each type of assortment.

3. Find the cost of production for each type of assortment.

4. Find the cost to fill the order.

Algebra 2

Matrix Multiplication

A furniture manufacturer makes upholstered chairs and wood tables. Matrix A shows the number of hours spent on each item by three different workers. One day the factory receives an order for 10 chairs and 3 tables. This is shown in matrix B.

$$\begin{array}{c} \text{hours} \\ \begin{array}{ccc} \text{woodworker} & \text{finisher} & \text{upholsterer} \end{array} \\ \begin{array}{c} \text{chair} \\ \text{table} \end{array} \begin{bmatrix} 4 & 2 & 12 \\ 18 & 15 & 0 \end{bmatrix} = A \end{array} \qquad \begin{array}{c} \begin{array}{cc} \text{chair} & \text{table} \end{array} \\ \text{number ordered } [\, 10 \quad 3\,] = B \end{array}$$

$$[10 \quad 3]\begin{bmatrix} 4 & 2 & 12 \\ 18 & 15 & 0 \end{bmatrix} = [10(4) + 3(18) \quad 10(2) + 3(15) \quad 10(12) + 3(0)] = [94 \quad 65 \quad 120]$$

The product of the two matrices shows the number of hours needed for each type of worker to complete the order: 94 hours for woodworking, 65 hours for finishing, and 120 hours for upholstering.

To find the total labor cost, multiply by a matrix that shows the hourly rate for each worker: $15 for woodworking, $9 for finishing, and $12 for upholstering.

$$C = \begin{bmatrix} 15 \\ 9 \\ 12 \end{bmatrix} \quad [94 \quad 65 \quad 120]\begin{bmatrix} 15 \\ 9 \\ 12 \end{bmatrix} = [94(15) + 65(9) + 120(12)] = \$3435$$

Use matrix multiplication to solve this problem.

A candy company packages caramels, chocolates, and hard candy in three different assortments: traditional, deluxe, and superb. For each type of candy the table below gives the number in each assortment, the number of Calories per piece, and the cost to make each piece.

	traditional	deluxe	superb	Calories per piece	cost per piece in cents
caramels	10	16	15	60	10
chocolates	12	8	25	70	12
hard candy	10	16	8	55	6

The company receives an order for 300 traditional, 180 deluxe and 100 superb assortments.

1. Find the number of each type of candy needed to fill the order.
   7380 caramels; 7540 chocolates; 6680 hard candies
2. Find the total number of Calories in each type of assortment.
   1990-traditional; 2400-deluxe; 3090-superb
3. Find the cost of production for each type of assortment.
   $3.04-traditional; $3.52-deluxe; $4.98-superb
4. Find the cost to fill the order. **$2043.60**

Enrichment

Percentiles

This table shows test scores and their frequencies. The frequency is the number of people who had a particular score. The cumulative frequency is the total frequency up to that point, starting at the lowest score and adding up.

Score	Frequency	Cumulative Frequency
95	1	50
90	2	49
85	5	47
80	6	42
75	7	36
70	8	29
65	7	21
60	6	14
55	4	8
50	3	4
45	1	1

Example 1: What score is at the 16th percentile?

A score at the 16th percentile means the score just above the lowest 16% of the scores.
16% of the 50 scores is 8 scores.
The 8th score is 55.
The score just above this is 56.
The score at the 16th percentile is 56.

Notice that no one had a score of 56 points.

Use the table above to find the score at each percentile.

1. 42nd percentile _____

2. 70th percentile _____

3. 33rd percentile _____

4. 90th percentile _____

5. 58th percentile _____

6. 80th percentile _____

Example 2: At what percentile is a score of 75?

There are 29 scores below 75.

Seven scores are at 75. The fourth of these seven is the midpoint of this group.

Adding 4 scores to the 29 gives 33 scores.

33 out of 50 is 66%.

Thus, a score of 75 is at the 66th percentile.

Use the table above to find the percentile of each score.

7. a score of 50 _____

8. a score of 77 _____

9. a score of 85 _____

10. a score of 58 _____

11. a score of 62 _____

12. a score of 81 _____

Enrichment

Percentiles

This table shows test scores and their frequencies. The frequency is the number of people who had a particular score. The cumulative frequency is the total frequency up to that point, starting at the lowest score and adding up.

Score	Frequency	Cumulative Frequency
95	1	50
90	2	49
85	5	47
80	6	42
75	7	36
70	8	29
65	7	21
60	6	14
55	4	8
50	3	4
45	1	1

Example 1: What score is at the 16th percentile?

A score at the 16th percentile means the score just above the lowest 16% of the scores.
16% of the 50 scores is 8 scores.
The 8th score is 55.
The score just above this is 56.
The score at the 16th percentile is 56.

Notice that no one had a score of 56 points.

Use the table above to find the score at each percentile.

1. 42nd percentile __66__
2. 70th percentile __76__
3. 33rd percentile __66__
4. 90th percentile __86__
5. 58th percentile __71__
6. 80th percentile __81__

Example 2: At what percentile is a score of 75?

There are 29 scores below 75.

Seven scores are at 75. The fourth of these seven is the midpoint of this group.

Adding 4 scores to the 29 gives 33 scores.

33 out of 50 is 66%.

Thus, a score of 75 is at the 66th percentile.

Use the table above to find the percentile of each score.

7. a score of 50 __6th__
8. a score of 77 __72nd__
9. a score of 85 __90th__
10. a score of 58 __16th__
11. a score of 62 __28th__
12. a score of 81 __84th__

Enrichment

Working with Exponents

The rules about powers and exponents are usually given with letters such as m, n, and k to represent exponents. For example, one rule states that $a^m \cdot a^n = a^{m+n}$.

In practice, such exponents are handled as algebraic expressions and the rules of algebra apply.

Example: Simplify $2a^2(a^{n+1} + a^{4n})$.

$$2a^2(a^{n+1} + a^{4n}) = 2a^2 \cdot a^{n+1} + 2a^2 \cdot a^{4n} \qquad \text{Use the distributive law.}$$

$$= 2a^{2+n+1} + 2a^{2+4n} \qquad \text{Recall } a^m \cdot a^n = a^{m+n}.$$

$$= 2a^{n+3} + 2a^{2+4n} \qquad \text{Simplify the exponent}$$
$$2 + n + 1 \text{ as } n + 3.$$

It is important always to collect *like* terms only.

Example: Simplify $(a^n + b^m)^2$.

$$(a^n + b^m)^2 = (a^n + b^m)(a^n + b^m)$$

$$\qquad\qquad F \qquad\quad O \qquad\quad I \qquad\quad L$$

$$= a^n \cdot a^n + a^n \cdot b^m + a^n \cdot b^m + b^m \cdot b^m \qquad \text{The second and third}$$
$$\text{terms are like terms.}$$

$$= a^{2n} + 2a^n b^m + b^{2m}$$

Simplify each expression by performing the indicated operations.

1. $2^3 2^m$

2. $(a^3)^n$

3. $(4^n b^2)^k$

4. $(x^3 a^j)^m$

5. $(-ay^n)^3$

6. $(-b^k x)^2$

7. $(c^2)^{hk}$

8. $(-2d^n)^5$

9. $(a^2 b)(a^n b^2)$

10. $(x^n y^m)(x^m y^n)$

11. $\dfrac{a^n}{a^2}$

12. $\dfrac{12x^3}{4x^n}$

13. $(ab^2 - a^2 b)(3a^n + 4b^n)$

14. $ab^2(2a^2 b^{n-1} + 4ab^n + 6b^{n+1})$

Enrichment

Working with Exponents

The rules about powers and exponents are usually given with letters such as m, n, and k to represent exponents. For example, one rule states that $a^m \cdot a^n = a^{m+n}$.

In practice, such exponents are handled as algebraic expressions and the rules of algebra apply.

Example: Simplify $2a^2(a^{n+1} + a^{4n})$.

$$2a^2(a^{n+1} + a^{4n}) = 2a^2 \cdot a^{n+1} + 2a^2 \cdot a^{4n}$$ **Use the distributive law.**

$$= 2a^{2+n+1} + 2a^{2+4n}$$ **Recall $a^m \cdot a^n = a^{m+n}$.**

$$= 2a^{n+3} + 2a^{2+4n}$$ **Simplify the exponent $2 + n + 1$ as $n + 3$.**

It is important always to collect *like* terms only.

Example: Simplify $(a^n + b^m)^2$.

$$(a^n + b^m)^2 = (a^n + b^m)(a^n + b^m)$$

$$\qquad\quad F \qquad O \qquad I \qquad L$$

$$= a^n \cdot a^n + a^n \cdot b^m + a^n \cdot b^m + b^m \cdot b^m$$ **The second and third terms are like terms.**

$$= a^{2n} + 2a^n b^m + b^{2m}$$

Simplify each expression by performing the indicated operations.

1. $2^3 2^m$ $\mathbf{2^{3+m}}$

2. $(a^3)^n$ $\mathbf{a^{3n}}$

3. $(4^n b^2)^k$ $\mathbf{4^{kn} b^{2k}}$

4. $(x^3 a^j)^m$ $\mathbf{x^{3m} a^{jm}}$

5. $(-ay^n)^3$ $\mathbf{-a^3 y^{3n}}$

6. $(-b^k x)^2$ $\mathbf{-b^{2k} x^2}$

7. $(c^2)^{hk}$ $\mathbf{c^{2hk}}$

8. $(-2d^n)^5$ $\mathbf{-32d^{5n}}$

9. $(a^2 b)(a^n b^2)$ $\mathbf{a^{2+n} b^3}$

10. $(x^n y^m)(x^m y^n)$ $\mathbf{x^{n+m} y^{n+m}}$ **11.** $\dfrac{a^n}{a^2}$ $\mathbf{a^{n-2}}$

12. $\dfrac{12x^3}{4x^n}$ $\mathbf{3x^{3-n}}$

13. $(ab^2 - a^2 b)(3a^n + 4b^n)$
$\mathbf{3a^{n+1} b^2 + 4ab^{n+2} - 3a^{n+2} b - 4a^2 b^{n+1}}$

14. $ab^2(2a^2 b^{n-1} + 4ab^n + 6b^{n+1})$
$\mathbf{2a^3 b^{n+1} + 4a^2 b^{n+2} + 6ab^{n+3}}$

Enrichment

Polynomials with Fractional Coefficients

Polynomials may have fractional coefficients as long as there are no variables in the denominators. Computing with fractional coefficients is performed in the same way as computing with whole-number coefficients.

Add, subtract, or multiply. Write all coefficients as fractions.

1. Add $\frac{3}{4}a + \frac{2}{5}b - \frac{1}{3}c$ and $\frac{1}{6}a - \frac{4}{3}b + \frac{5}{7}c$.

2. Subtract $\frac{7}{3}p - \frac{5}{2}m - \frac{3}{4}n$ from $\frac{3}{5}m - \frac{2}{7}p - \frac{1}{3}n$.

3. Add $\frac{3}{2}x - \frac{4}{3}y - \frac{5}{4}z$, $-\frac{1}{4}x + y + \frac{2}{5}z$, and $-\frac{7}{8}x - \frac{6}{7}y + \frac{1}{2}z$.

4. Add $\frac{1}{2}a^2 - \frac{1}{3}ab + \frac{1}{4}b^2$ and $\frac{5}{6}a^2 + \frac{2}{3}ab - \frac{3}{4}b^2$.

5. From $\frac{1}{2}a^2 - \frac{1}{3}ab + \frac{1}{4}b^2$ take $\frac{1}{3}a^2 - \frac{1}{2}ab + \frac{5}{6}b^2$.

6. Multiply $\frac{1}{2}a^2 - \frac{1}{3}ab + \frac{1}{4}b^2$ by $\frac{1}{2}a - \frac{2}{3}b$.

7. Multiply $\frac{2}{3}a^2 - \frac{1}{5}a + \frac{2}{7}$ by $\frac{2}{3}a^3 + \frac{1}{5}a^2 - \frac{2}{7}a$.

8. Multiply $\frac{2}{3}x^2 - \frac{3}{4}x - 2$ by $\frac{4}{5}x - \frac{1}{6}x^2 - \frac{1}{2}$.

9. Multiply $\frac{1}{6} + \frac{1}{3}x + \frac{1}{6}x^4 - \frac{1}{2}x^2$ by $\frac{1}{6}x^3 - \frac{1}{3} - \frac{1}{3}x$.

5-2

Enrichment

Student Edition
Pages 261–266

Polynomials with Fractional Coefficients

Polynomials may have fractional coefficients as long as there are
no variables in the denominators. Computing with fractional
coefficients is performed in the same way as computing with
whole-number coefficients.

Add, subtract, or multiply. Write all coefficients as fractions.

1. Add $\frac{3}{4}a + \frac{2}{5}b - \frac{1}{3}c$ and $\frac{1}{6}a - \frac{4}{3}b + \frac{5}{7}c$.

$\frac{11}{12}a - \frac{14}{15}b + \frac{8}{21}c$

2. Subtract $\frac{7}{3}p - \frac{5}{2}m - \frac{3}{4}n$ from $\frac{3}{5}m - \frac{2}{7}p - \frac{1}{3}n$.

$\frac{31}{10}m + \frac{5}{12}n - \frac{55}{21}p$

3. Add $\frac{3}{2}x - \frac{4}{3}y - \frac{5}{4}z$, $-\frac{1}{4}x + y + \frac{2}{5}z$, and $-\frac{7}{8}x - \frac{6}{7}y + \frac{1}{2}z$.

$\frac{3}{8}x - \frac{25}{21}y - \frac{7}{20}z$

4. Add $\frac{1}{2}a^2 - \frac{1}{3}ab + \frac{1}{4}b^2$ and $\frac{5}{6}a^2 + \frac{2}{3}ab - \frac{3}{4}b^2$.

$\frac{4}{3}a^2 + \frac{1}{3}ab - \frac{1}{2}b^2$

5. From $\frac{1}{2}a^2 - \frac{1}{3}ab + \frac{1}{4}b^2$ take $\frac{1}{3}a^2 - \frac{1}{2}ab + \frac{5}{6}b^2$.

$\frac{1}{6}a^2 + \frac{1}{6}ab - \frac{7}{12}b^2$

6. Multiply $\frac{1}{2}a^2 - \frac{1}{3}ab + \frac{1}{4}b^2$ by $\frac{1}{2}a - \frac{2}{3}b$.

$\frac{1}{4}a^3 - \frac{1}{2}a^2b + \frac{25}{72}ab^2 - \frac{1}{6}b^3$

7. Multiply $\frac{2}{3}a^2 - \frac{1}{5}a + \frac{2}{7}$ by $\frac{2}{3}a^3 + \frac{1}{5}a^2 - \frac{2}{7}a$.

$\frac{4}{9}a^5 - \frac{1}{25}a^3 + \frac{4}{35}a^2 - \frac{4}{49}a$

8. Multiply $\frac{2}{3}x^2 - \frac{3}{4}x - 2$ by $\frac{4}{5}x - \frac{1}{6}x^2 - \frac{1}{2}$.

$-\frac{1}{9}x^4 + \frac{79}{120}x^3 - \frac{3}{5}x^2 - \frac{49}{40}x + 1$

9. Multiply $\frac{1}{6} + \frac{1}{3}x + \frac{1}{6}x^4 - \frac{1}{2}x^2$ by $\frac{1}{6}x^3 - \frac{1}{3} - \frac{1}{3}x$.

$\frac{1}{36}x^7 - \frac{5}{36}x^5 + \frac{7}{36}x^3 + \frac{1}{18}x^2 - \frac{1}{6}x - \frac{1}{18}$

Algebra 2

5-3

Enrichment

Oblique Asymptotes

The graph of $y = ax + b$, where $a \neq 0$, is called an oblique
asymptote of $y = f(x)$ if the graph of f comes closer and closer to
the line as $x \to \infty$ or $x \to -\infty$.

For $f(x) = 3x + 4 + \dfrac{2}{x}$, $y = 3x + 4$ is an oblique asymptote because

$f(x) - 3x - 4 = \dfrac{2}{x}$, and $\dfrac{2}{x} \to 0$ as $x \to \infty$ or $-\infty$.

Example: Find the oblique asymptote for $f(x) = \dfrac{x^2 + 8x + 15}{x + 2}$.

$$
\begin{array}{r|rrr}
-2 & 1 & 8 & 15 \\
   &   & -2 & -12 \\
\hline
   & 1 & 6 & \,|\ 3
\end{array}
\qquad
\begin{array}{l}
\text{Use synthetic} \\
\text{division.}
\end{array}
$$

$$y = \frac{x^2 + 8x + 15}{x + 2} = x + 6 + \frac{3}{x - 2}$$

Since $\dfrac{3}{x - 2} \to 0$ as $x \to \infty$ or $x \to -\infty$, $y = x + 6$ is an oblique asymptote.

**Use synthetic division to find the oblique asymptote for each of
the following.**

1. $y = \dfrac{8x^2 - 4x + 11}{x + 5}$

2. $y = \dfrac{x^2 + 3x - 15}{x - 2}$

3. $y = \dfrac{x^2 - 2x - 18}{x - 3}$

4. $y = \dfrac{ax^2 + bx + c}{x - d}$

5. $y = \dfrac{ax^2 + bx + c}{x + d}$

Oblique Asymptotes

The graph of $y = ax + b$, where $a \neq 0$, is called an oblique asymptote of $y = f(x)$ if the graph of f comes closer and closer to the line as $x \to \infty$ or $x \to -\infty$.

For $f(x) = 3x + 4 + \dfrac{2}{x}$, $y = 3x + 4$ is an oblique asymptote because $f(x) - 3x - 4 = \dfrac{2}{x}$, and $\dfrac{2}{x} \to 0$ as $x \to \infty$ or $-\infty$.

Example: Find the oblique asymptote for $f(x) = \dfrac{x^2 + 8x + 15}{x + 2}$.

$$
\begin{array}{r|rrr}
-2 & 1 & 8 & 15 \\
   &   & -2 & -12 \\
\hline
   & 1 & 6 & \; 3
\end{array}
$$

Use synthetic division.

$$y = \frac{x^2 + 8x + 15}{x + 2} = x + 6 + \frac{3}{x - 2}$$

Since $\dfrac{3}{x - 2} \to 0$ as $x \to \infty$ or $x \to -\infty$, $y = x + 6$ is an oblique asymptote.

Use synthetic division to find the oblique asymptote for each of the following.

1. $y = \dfrac{8x^2 - 4x + 11}{x + 5}$ **y = 8x − 44**

2. $y = \dfrac{x^2 + 3x - 15}{x - 2}$ **y = x + 5**

3. $y = \dfrac{x^2 - 2x - 18}{x - 3}$ **y = x + 1**

4. $y = \dfrac{ax^2 + bx + c}{x - d}$ **y = ax + b + ad**

5. $y = \dfrac{ax^2 + bx + c}{x + d}$ **y = ax + b − ad**

Enrichment

Sums and Differences of Odd Powers

Study the patterns below for factoring the sum and the difference of cubes.

$a^3 + b^3 = (a + b)(a^2 - ab + b^2)$
$a^3 - b^3 = (a - b)(a^2 + ab + b^2)$

This pattern can be extended to other odd powers. Study these examples.

Example: Factor $a^5 + b^5$.
Extend the first pattern to obtain $a^5 + b^5 = (a + b)(a^4 - a^3b + a^2b^2 - ab^3 + b^4)$.
Check: $(a + b)(a^4 - a^3b + a^2b^2 - ab^3 + b^4) = a^5 - a^4b + a^3b^2 - a^2b^3 + ab^4$
$$\underline{\hspace{4cm} + a^4b - a^3b^2 + a^2b^3 - ab^4 + b^5}$$
$$= a^5 \hspace{6cm} + b^5$$

Example: Factor $a^5 - b^5$.
Extend the second pattern to obtain $a^5 - b^5 = (a - b)(a^4 + a^3b + a^2b^2 + ab^3 + b^4)$.
Check: $(a - b)(a^4 + a^3b + a^2b^2 + ab^3 + b^4) = a^5 + a^4b + a^3b^2 + a^2b^3 + ab^4$
$$\underline{\hspace{4cm} - a^4b - a^3b^2 - a^2b^3 - ab^4 - b^5}$$
$$= a^5 \hspace{6cm} - b^5$$

In general, if n is an odd integer, when you factor $a^n + b^n$ or $a^n - b^n$, one factor will be either $(a + b)$ or $(a - b)$, depending on the sign of the original expression. The other factor will have the following properties:
- The first term will be a^{n-1} and the last term will be b^{n-1}.
- The exponents of a will decrease by 1 as you go from left to right.
- The exponents of b will increase by 1 as you go from left to right.
- The degree of each term will be $n - 1$.
- If the original expression was $a^n + b^n$, the terms will alternately have $+$ and $-$ signs.
- If the original expression was $a^n - b^n$, the terms will all have $+$ signs.

Use the patterns above to factor each expression.

1. $a^7 + b^7$

2. $c^9 - d^9$

3. $e^{11} + f^{11}$

To factor an expression such as $x^{10} - y^{10}$, you can first change it to $(x^5 + y^5)(x^5 - y^5)$, then factor each part. Use this approach to factor each expression.

4. $x^{10} - y^{10}$

5. $a^{14} - b^{14}$

Algebra 2

Enrichment

Sums and Differences of Odd Powers

Study the patterns below for factoring the sum and the difference
of cubes.

$a^3 + b^3 = (a + b)(a^2 - ab + b^2)$

$a^3 - b^3 = (a - b)(a^2 + ab + b^2)$

This pattern can be extended to other odd powers. Study these examples.

Example: Factor $a^5 + b^5$.

Extend the first pattern to obtain $a^5 + b^5 = (a + b)(a^4 - a^3b + a^2b^2 - ab^3 + b^4)$.

Check: $(a + b)(a^4 - a^3b + a^2b^2 - ab^3 + b^4) = a^5 - a^4b + a^3b^2 - a^2b^3 + ab^4$

$$+ a^4b - a^3b^2 + a^2b^3 - ab^4 + b^5$$

$$= a^5 \qquad\qquad\qquad\qquad\qquad + b^5$$

Example: Factor $a^5 - b^5$.

Extend the second pattern to obtain $a^5 - b^5 = (a - b)(a^4 + a^3b + a^2b^2 + ab^3 + b^4)$.

Check: $(a - b)(a^4 + a^3b + a^2b^2 + ab^3 + b^4) = a^5 + a^4b + a^3b^2 + a^2b^3 + ab^4$

$$- a^4b - a^3b^2 - a^2b^3 - ab^4 - b^5$$

$$= a^5 \qquad\qquad\qquad\qquad\qquad - b^5$$

In general, if n is an odd integer, when you factor $a^n + b^n$ or $a^n - b^n$, one factor will be
either $(a + b)$ or $(a - b)$, depending on the sign of the original expression. The other
factor will have the following properties:

- The first term will be a^{n-1} and the last term will be b^{n-1}.
- The exponents of a will decrease by 1 as you go from left to right.
- The exponents of b will increase by 1 as you go from left to right.
- The degree of each term will be $n - 1$.
- If the original expression was $a^n + b^n$, the terms will alternately have + and − signs.
- If the original expression was $a^n - b^n$, the terms will all have + signs.

Use the patterns above to factor each expression.

1. $a^7 + b^7$ $(a + b)(a^6 - a^5b + a^4b^2 - a^3b^3 + a^2b^4 - ab^5 + b^6)$

2. $c^9 - d^9$ $(c - d)(c^8 + c^7d + c^6d^2 + c^5d^3 + c^4d^4 + c^3d^5 + c^2d^6 + cd^7 + d^8)$

3. $e^{11} + f^{11}$ $(e + f)(e^{10} - e^9f + e^8f^2 - e^7f^3 + e^6f^4 - e^5f^5 + e^4f^6 - e^3f^7 + e^2f^8 -$
$$ef^9 + f^{10})$$

**To factor an expression such as $x^{10} - y^{10}$, you can first change it to $(x^5 + y^5)(x^5 - y^5)$,
then factor each part. Use this approach to factor each expression.**

4. $x^{10} - y^{10}$ $(x + y)(x^4 - x^3y + x^2y^2 - xy^3 + y^4)(x - y)(x^4 + x^3y + x^2y^2 + xy^3 + y^4)$

5. $a^{14} - b^{14}$ $(a + b)(a^6 - a^5b + a^4b^2 - a^3b^3 + a^2b^4 - ab^5 + b^6)(a - b)$
$$(a^6 + a^5b + a^4b^2 + a^3b^3 + a^2b^4 + ab^5 + b^6)$$

NAME_____ DATE _____

Enrichment

Approximating Square Roots

Consider the following expansion.

$$\left(a + \frac{b}{2a}\right)^2 = a^2 + \frac{2ab}{2a} + \frac{b^2}{4a^2}$$

$$= a^2 + b + \frac{b^2}{4a^2}$$

Think what happens if a is very great in comparison to b. The term $\frac{b^2}{4a^2}$ is very small and can be disregarded in an approximation.

$$\left(a + \frac{b}{2a}\right)^2 \approx a^2 + b$$

$$a + \frac{b}{2a} \approx \sqrt{a^2 + b}$$

Suppose a number can be expressed as $a^2 + b$, $a > b$. Then an approximate value of the square root is $a + \frac{b}{2a}$.

You should also see that $a - \frac{b}{2a} \approx \sqrt{a^2 - b}$.

Examples: Use the formula $\sqrt{a^2 \pm b} \approx a \pm \frac{b}{2a}$ to find approximations for $\sqrt{101}$ and $\sqrt{622}$.

a. $\sqrt{101} = \sqrt{100 + 1} = \sqrt{10^2 + 1}$

Let $a = 10$ and $b = 1$.

$$\sqrt{101} \approx 10 + \frac{1}{2(10)}$$

$$\approx 10.05$$

b. $\sqrt{622} = \sqrt{625 - 3} = \sqrt{25^2 - 3}$

Let $a = 25$ and $b = 3$.

$$\sqrt{622} \approx 25 - \frac{3}{2(25)}$$

$$\approx 24.94$$

Find an approximation for each square root to the nearest hundredth.

1. $\sqrt{626}$

2. $\sqrt{99}$

3. $\sqrt{402}$

4. $\sqrt{1604}$

5. $\sqrt{223}$

6. $\sqrt{80}$

7. $\sqrt{4890}$

8. $\sqrt{2505}$

9. $\sqrt{3575}$

10. $\sqrt{1,441,100}$

11. $\sqrt{290}$

12. $\sqrt{260}$

13. Show that $a - \frac{b}{2a} \approx \sqrt{a^2 - b}$ for $a > b$.

Algebra 2

Enrichment

Approximating Square Roots

Consider the following expansion.

$$\left(a + \frac{b}{2a}\right)^2 = a^2 + \frac{2ab}{2a} + \frac{b^2}{4a^2}$$

$$= a^2 + b + \frac{b^2}{4a^2}$$

Think what happens if a is very great in comparison to b. The term $\frac{b^2}{4a^2}$ is very small and can be disregarded in an approximation.

$$\left(a + \frac{b}{2a}\right)^2 \approx a^2 + b$$

$$a + \frac{b}{2a} \approx \sqrt{a^2 + b}$$

Suppose a number can be expressed as $a^2 + b$, $a > b$. Then an approximate value of the square root is $a + \frac{b}{2a}$.

You should also see that $a - \frac{b}{2a} \approx \sqrt{a^2 - b}$.

Examples: Use the formula $\sqrt{a^2 \pm b} \approx a \pm \frac{b}{2a}$ to find approximations for $\sqrt{101}$ and $\sqrt{622}$.

a. $\sqrt{101} = \sqrt{100 + 1} = \sqrt{10^2 + 1}$

Let $a = 10$ and $b = 1$.

$$\sqrt{101} \approx 10 + \frac{1}{2(10)}$$

$$\approx 10.05$$

b. $\sqrt{622} = \sqrt{625 - 3} = \sqrt{25^2 - 3}$

Let $a = 25$ and $b = 3$.

$$\sqrt{622} \approx 25 - \frac{3}{2(25)}$$

$$\approx 24.94$$

Find an approximation for each square root to the nearest hundredth.

1. $\sqrt{626}$ **25.02**

2. $\sqrt{99}$ **9.95**

3. $\sqrt{402}$ **20.05**

4. $\sqrt{1604}$ **40.05**

5. $\sqrt{223}$ **14.93**

6. $\sqrt{80}$ **8.94**

7. $\sqrt{4890}$ **69.93**

8. $\sqrt{2505}$ **50.05**

9. $\sqrt{3575}$ **59.79**

10. $\sqrt{1,441,100}$ **1200.42**

11. $\sqrt{290}$ **17.03**

12. $\sqrt{260}$ **16.12**

13. Show that $a - \frac{b}{2a} \approx \sqrt{a^2 - b}$ for $a > b$. $\left(a - \frac{b}{2a}\right)^2 = a^2 - b + \frac{b^2}{4a^2}$;

disregard $\frac{b^2}{4a^2}$; $\left(a - \frac{b}{2a}\right)^2 \approx a^2 - b$; $a - \frac{b}{2a} \approx \sqrt{a^2 - b}$

Special Products with Radicals

Notice that $(\sqrt{3})(\sqrt{3}) = 3$, or $(\sqrt{3})^2 = 3$.

In general, $(\sqrt{x})^2 = x$ when $x \geq 0$.

Also, notice that $(\sqrt{9})(\sqrt{4}) = \sqrt{36}$.

In general, $(\sqrt{x})(\sqrt{y}) = \sqrt{xy}$ when x and y are not negative.

You can use these ideas to find the special products below.

$$(\sqrt{a} + \sqrt{b})(\sqrt{a} - \sqrt{b}) = (\sqrt{a})^2 - (\sqrt{b})^2 = a - b$$
$$(\sqrt{a} + \sqrt{b})^2 = (\sqrt{a})^2 + 2\sqrt{ab} + (\sqrt{b})_2 = a + 2\sqrt{ab} + b$$
$$(\sqrt{a} - \sqrt{b})^2 = (\sqrt{a})^2 - 2\sqrt{ab} + (\sqrt{b})^2 = a - 2\sqrt{ab} + b$$

Example: Find the product: $(\sqrt{2} + \sqrt{5})(\sqrt{2} - \sqrt{5})$.

$$(\sqrt{2} + \sqrt{5})(\sqrt{2} - \sqrt{5}) = (\sqrt{2})^2 - (\sqrt{5})^2 = 2 - 5 = -3$$

Example: Evaluate $(\sqrt{2} + \sqrt{8})^2$.

$$(\sqrt{2} + \sqrt{8})^2 = (\sqrt{2})^2 + 2\sqrt{2}\sqrt{8} + (\sqrt{8})^2$$
$$= 2 + 2\sqrt{16} + 8 = 2 + 2(4) + 8 = 2 + 8 + 8 = 18$$

Multiply.

1. $(\sqrt{3} - \sqrt{7})(\sqrt{3} + \sqrt{7})$

2. $(\sqrt{10} + \sqrt{2})(\sqrt{10} - \sqrt{2})$

3. $(\sqrt{2x} - \sqrt{6})(\sqrt{2x} + \sqrt{6})$

4. $(\sqrt{3} - \sqrt{27})^2$

5. $(\sqrt{1000} + \sqrt{10})^2$

6. $(\sqrt{y} + \sqrt{5})(\sqrt{y} - \sqrt{5})$

7. $(\sqrt{50} - \sqrt{x})^2$

8. $(\sqrt{x} + \sqrt{20})^2$

You can extend these ideas to patterns for sums and differences of cubes. Study the pattern below.

$$(\sqrt[3]{8} - \sqrt[3]{x})(\sqrt[3]{8^2} + \sqrt[3]{8x} + \sqrt[3]{x^2}) = (\sqrt[3]{8})^3 - \sqrt[3]{x^3}) = 8 - x$$

Multiply.

9. $(\sqrt[3]{2} - \sqrt[3]{5})(\sqrt[3]{2^2} + \sqrt[3]{10} + \sqrt[3]{5^2})$

10. $(\sqrt[3]{y} + \sqrt[3]{w})(\sqrt[3]{y^2} - \sqrt[3]{yw} + \sqrt[3]{w^2})$

11. $(\sqrt[3]{7} + \sqrt[3]{20})(\sqrt[3]{7^2} - \sqrt[3]{140} + \sqrt[3]{20^2})$

12. $(\sqrt[3]{11} - \sqrt[3]{8})(\sqrt[3]{11^2} + \sqrt[3]{88} + \sqrt[3]{8^2})$

Enrichment

Special Products with Radicals

Notice that $(\sqrt{3})(\sqrt{3}) = 3$, or $(\sqrt{3})^2 = 3$.

In general, $(\sqrt{x})^2 = x$ when $x \geq 0$.

Also, notice that $(\sqrt{9})(\sqrt{4}) = \sqrt{36}$.

In general, $(\sqrt{x})(\sqrt{y}) = \sqrt{xy}$ when x and y are not negative.

You can use these ideas to find the special products below.

$$(\sqrt{a} + \sqrt{b})(\sqrt{a} - \sqrt{b}) = (\sqrt{a})^2 - (\sqrt{b})^2 = a - b$$
$$(\sqrt{a} + \sqrt{b})^2 = (\sqrt{a})^2 + 2\sqrt{ab} + (\sqrt{b})^2 = a + 2\sqrt{ab} + b$$
$$(\sqrt{a} - \sqrt{b})^2 = (\sqrt{a})^2 - 2\sqrt{ab} + (\sqrt{b})^2 = a - 2\sqrt{ab} + b$$

Example: Find the product: $(\sqrt{2} + \sqrt{5})(\sqrt{2} - \sqrt{5})$.

$$(\sqrt{2} + \sqrt{5})(\sqrt{2} - \sqrt{5}) = (\sqrt{2})^2 - (\sqrt{5})^2 = 2 - 5 = -3$$

Example: Evaluate $(\sqrt{2} + \sqrt{8})^2$.

$$(\sqrt{2} + \sqrt{8})^2 = (\sqrt{2})^2 + 2\sqrt{2}\sqrt{8} + (\sqrt{8})^2$$
$$= 2 + 2\sqrt{16} + 8 = 2 + 2(4) + 8 = 2 + 8 + 8 = 18$$

Multiply.

1. $(\sqrt{3} - \sqrt{7})(\sqrt{3} + \sqrt{7})$ **−4**

2. $(\sqrt{10} + \sqrt{2})(\sqrt{10} - \sqrt{2})$ **8**

3. $(\sqrt{2x} - \sqrt{6})(\sqrt{2x} + \sqrt{6})$ **2x − 6**

4. $(\sqrt{3} - \sqrt{27})^2$ **12**

5. $(\sqrt{1000} + \sqrt{10})^2$ **1210**

6. $(\sqrt{y} + \sqrt{5})(\sqrt{y} - \sqrt{5})$ **y − 5**

7. $(\sqrt{50} - \sqrt{x})^2$ **50 − 10$\sqrt{2x}$ + x**

8. $(\sqrt{x} + \sqrt{20})^2$ **x + 4$\sqrt{5x}$ + 20**

You can extend these ideas to patterns for sums and differences of cubes. Study the pattern below.

$$(\sqrt[3]{8} - \sqrt[3]{x})(\sqrt[3]{8^2} + \sqrt[3]{8x} + \sqrt[3]{x^2}) = (\sqrt[3]{8})^3 - \sqrt[3]{x^3} = 8 - x$$

Multiply.

9. $(\sqrt[3]{2} - \sqrt[3]{5})(\sqrt[3]{2^2} + \sqrt[3]{10} + \sqrt[3]{5^2})$ **−3**

10. $(\sqrt[3]{y} + \sqrt[3]{w})(\sqrt[3]{y^2} - \sqrt[3]{yw} + \sqrt[3]{w^2})$ **y + w**

11. $(\sqrt[3]{7} + \sqrt[3]{20})(\sqrt[3]{7^2} - \sqrt[3]{140} + \sqrt[3]{20^2})$ **27**

12. $(\sqrt[3]{11} - \sqrt[3]{8})(\sqrt[3]{11^2} + \sqrt[3]{88} + \sqrt[3]{8^2})$ **3**

 Algebra 2

Enrichment

Lesser-Known Geometric Formulas

Many geometric formulas involve radical expressions.

Make a drawing to illustrate each of the formulas given on this page.

1. The area of an isosceles triangle. Two sides have length a; the other side has length of c.

$$A = \frac{c}{4}\sqrt{4a^2 - c^2}$$

2. The area of an equilateral triangle with a side of length a.

$$A = \frac{a^2}{4}\sqrt{3}$$

3. The area of a regular pentagon with a side of length a.

$$A = \frac{a^2}{4}\sqrt{25 + 10\sqrt{5}}$$

4. The area of a regular hexagon with a side of length a.

$$A = \frac{3a^2}{2}\sqrt{3}$$

5. The volume of a regular tetrahedron with an edge of length a.

$$V = \frac{a^3}{12}\sqrt{2}$$

6. The area of the curved surface of a right cone with an altitude of h and radius of base r.

$$S = \pi r\sqrt{r^2 + h^2}$$

7. Heron's Formula for the area of a triangle uses the semi-perimeter s, where $s = \frac{a + b + c}{2}$. The sides of the triangle have lengths a, b, and c.

$$A = \sqrt{s(s - a)(s - b)(s - c)}$$

8. The radius of a circle inscribed in a given triangle also uses the semi-perimeter.

$$r = \frac{\sqrt{s(s - a)(s - b)(s - c)}}{s}$$

Algebra 2

NAME_____ DATE _____

Enrichment

Lesser-Known Geometric Formulas

Many geometric formulas involve radical expressions.

Make a drawing to illustrate each of the formulas given on this page.

1. The area of an isosceles triangle. Two sides have length a; the other side has length of c.

$$A = \frac{c}{4}\sqrt{4a^2 - c^2}$$

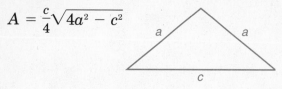

2. The area of an equilateral triangle with a side of length a.

$$A = \frac{a^2}{4}\sqrt{3}$$

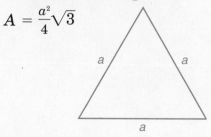

3. The area of a regular pentagon with a side of length a.

$$A = \frac{a^2}{4}\sqrt{25 + 10\sqrt{5}}$$

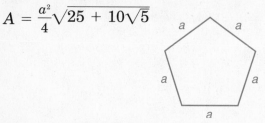

4. The area of a regular hexagon with a side of length a.

$$A = \frac{3a^2}{2}\sqrt{3}$$

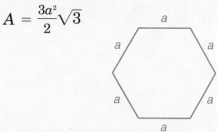

5. The volume of a regular tetrahedron with an edge of length a.

$$V = \frac{a^3}{12}\sqrt{2}$$

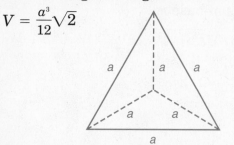

6. The area of the curved surface of a right cone with an altitude of h and radius of base r.

$$S = \pi r\sqrt{r^2 + h^2}$$

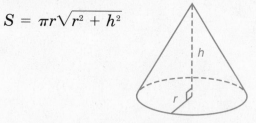

7. Heron's Formula for the area of a triangle uses the semi-perimeter s, where $s = \frac{a + b + c}{2}$. The sides of the triangle have lengths a, b, and c.

$$A = \sqrt{s(s - a)(s - b)(s - c)}$$

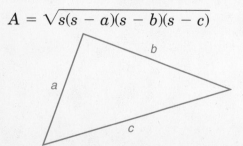

8. The radius of a circle inscribed in a given triangle also uses the semi-perimeter.

$$r = \frac{\sqrt{s(s - a)(s - b)(s - c)}}{s}$$

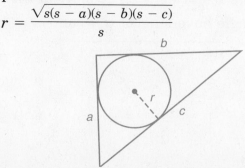

Algebra 2

Enrichment

Doubling

According to Thomas H. McMahon in the July 1975 issue of *Scientific American,* the height of a tree varies directly with the $\frac{2}{3}$ power of the radius of the trunk at its base. ($h = kr^{\frac{2}{3}}$ where k is a constant.) Suppose you own a stand of trees that can be used for making paper. The amount of wood pulp and therefore the value of the trees should be proportional to the volume of the trees. If we approximate a tree without its branches as a right circular cone, the formula for the volume of the tree is $\frac{1}{3}\pi r^2 h = \frac{1}{3}\pi r^2 (kr^{\frac{2}{3}}) = \frac{1}{3}\pi k r^{\frac{8}{3}}$.

If the trees on your land have radii of 3 inches and increase in radius one-fourth inch per year, it is possible to find the number of years it would take for the value of the trees to double.

$$\text{volume of one tree now} = \frac{1}{3}\pi k(3)^{\frac{8}{3}} = \frac{1}{3}\pi k \left(3 + \frac{1}{4} \cdot 0\right)^{\frac{8}{3}}$$

$$\text{volume of one tree after 1 year} = \frac{1}{3}\pi k \left(3 + \frac{1}{4} \cdot 1\right)^{\frac{8}{3}}$$

$$\text{volume of one tree after 2 years} = \frac{1}{3}\pi k \left(3 + \frac{1}{4} \cdot 2\right)^{\frac{8}{3}}$$

$$\vdots \qquad\qquad \vdots$$

$$\text{volume of one tree after } y \text{ years} = \frac{1}{3}\pi k \left(3 + \frac{1}{4} \cdot y\right)^{\frac{8}{3}}$$

We want the volume to double: $2(\text{present volume}) = 2 \cdot \frac{1}{3}\pi k \cdot 3^{\frac{8}{3}}$.

Therefore, we are looking for the value of y which makes the following equation true.

$$2 \cdot \frac{1}{3}\pi k \cdot 3^{\frac{8}{3}} = \frac{1}{3}\pi k \left(3 + \frac{1}{4}y\right)^{\frac{8}{3}} \text{ or } 2 \cdot \frac{1}{3}\pi k \cdot \sqrt[3]{3^8} = \frac{1}{3}\pi k \sqrt[3]{\left(3 + \frac{1}{4}y\right)^8}$$

Solve each problem.

1. Solve this equation for y, showing all work. Give a decimal approximation to the nearest tenth of a year.

2. According to the "Rule of 72," an investment at $p\%$ takes about $\frac{72}{p}$ years to double. In problem 1, what percent are you making on your investment?

3. Generalize the situation in problem 1. Let:
   m = the number of times you want the value to increase (In problem 1, $m = 2$.)
   r = the initial radius in inches (In problem 1, $r = 3$.)
   n = the number of inches the radius increases per year $\left(\text{In problem 1, } n = \frac{1}{4}.\right)$

   Derive the following formula. $y = \frac{r}{n}(m^{\frac{3}{8}} - 1)$

NAME_____ DATE _____

Enrichment

Doubling

According to Thomas H. McMahon in the July 1975 issue of *Scientific American,* the height of a tree varies directly with the $\frac{2}{3}$ power of the radius of the trunk at its base. ($h = kr^{\frac{2}{3}}$ where k is a constant.) Suppose you own a stand of trees that can be used for making paper. The amount of wood pulp and therefore the value of the trees should be proportional to the volume of the trees. If we approximate a tree without its branches as a right circular cone, the formula for the volume of the tree is $\frac{1}{3}\pi r^2 h = \frac{1}{3}\pi r^2 (kr^{\frac{2}{3}}) = \frac{1}{3}\pi k r^{\frac{8}{3}}$.

If the trees on your land have radii of 3 inches and increase in radius one-fourth inch per year, it is possible to find the number of years it would take for the value of the trees to double.

$$\text{volume of one tree now} = \frac{1}{3}\pi k(3)^{\frac{8}{3}} = \frac{1}{3}\pi k\left(3 + \frac{1}{4} \cdot 0\right)^{\frac{8}{3}}$$

$$\text{volume of one tree after 1 year} = \frac{1}{3}\pi k\left(3 + \frac{1}{4} \cdot 1\right)^{\frac{8}{3}}$$

$$\text{volume of one tree after 2 years} = \frac{1}{3}\pi k\left(3 + \frac{1}{4} \cdot 2\right)^{\frac{8}{3}}$$

$$\vdots \qquad\qquad \vdots$$

$$\text{volume of one tree after } y \text{ years} = \frac{1}{3}\pi k\left(3 + \frac{1}{4} \cdot y\right)^{\frac{8}{3}}$$

We want the volume to double: 2(present volume) $= 2 \cdot \frac{1}{3}\pi k \cdot 3^{\frac{8}{3}}$.

Therefore, we are looking for the value of y which makes the following equation true.

$$2 \cdot \frac{1}{3}\pi k \cdot 3^{\frac{8}{3}} = \frac{1}{3}\pi k\left(3 + \frac{1}{4}y\right)^{\frac{8}{3}} \text{ or } 2 \cdot \frac{1}{3}\pi k \cdot \sqrt[3]{3^8} = \frac{1}{3}\pi k \sqrt[3]{\left(3 + \frac{1}{4}y\right)^8}$$

Solve each problem.

1. Solve this equation for y, showing all work. Give a decimal approximation to the nearest tenth of a year. **$y = 3.6$**

2. According to the "Rule of 72," an investment at $p\%$ takes about $\frac{72}{p}$ years to double. In problem 1, what percent are you making on your investment? **$3.6 = \frac{72}{p}$; 20%**

3. Generalize the situation in problem 1. Let:
   m = the number of times you want the value to increase (In problem 1, $m = 2$.)
   r = the initial radius in inches (In problem 1, $r = 3$.)
   n = the number of inches the radius increases per year $\left(\text{In problem 1, } n = \frac{1}{4}.\right)$

   Derive the following formula. $y = \frac{r}{n}(m^{\frac{3}{8}} - 1)$ **$m \cdot \frac{1}{3}\pi k \cdot r^{\frac{8}{3}} = \frac{1}{3}\pi k(r + ny)^{\frac{8}{3}}$;**

   $mr^{\frac{8}{3}} = (r + ny)^{\frac{8}{3}}$; $m^3 r^8 = (r + ny)^8$; $m^{\frac{3}{8}}r = r + ny$; $\frac{r}{n}(m^{\frac{3}{8}} - 1) = y$

NAME_____ DATE _____

Enrichment

Graphing Complex Numbers

Every ordered pair of numbers (a, b) corresonds to exactly one complex number $a + bi$. Also, recall that every point in the coordinate plane corresponds to exactly one pair of numbers called the coordinates of the point.

Thus, a complex number $a + bi$ is associated with exactly one point of the plane called (a, b).

An arrow drawn from the origin to the point (a, b) represents the complex number $a + bi$.

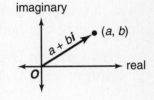

In the grid below each exercise, graph the complex numbers. The first exercise is completed for you.

1. $2 + 3i$ and $1 - 2i$

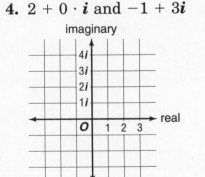

2. $1 + 4i$ and $2 + i$

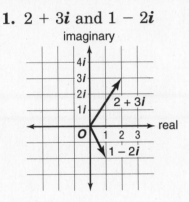

3. $-1 + 4i$ and $3 - 2i$

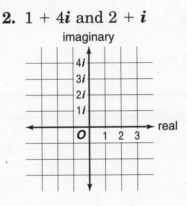

4. $2 + 0 \cdot i$ and $-1 + 3i$

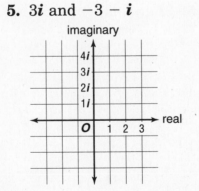

5. $3i$ and $-3 - i$

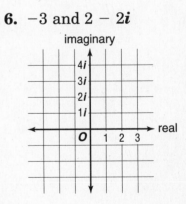

6. -3 and $2 - 2i$

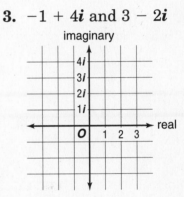

In each exercise, find the sum of the complex numbers in the exercise named. Then graph the sum in the grid for that exercise.

7. exercise 1

8. exercise 2

9. exercise 3

10. exercise 4

11. exercise 5

12. exercise 6

Algebra 2

NAME_____ DATE _____

Enrichment

Student Edition
Pages 310–316

Graphing Complex Numbers

Every ordered pair of numbers (a, b) corresonds to exactly one complex number $a + bi$. Also, recall that every point in the coordinate plane corresponds to exactly one pair of numbers called the coordinates of the point.

Thus, a complex number $a + bi$ is associated with exactly one point of the plane called (a, b).

An arrow drawn from the origin to the point (a, b) represents the complex number $a + bi$.

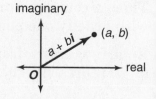

In the grid below each exercise, graph the complex numbers. The first exercise is completed for you.

1. $2 + 3i$ and $1 - 2i$

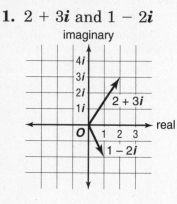

2. $1 + 4i$ and $2 + i$

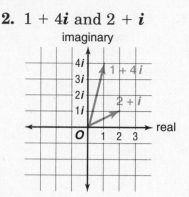

3. $-1 + 4i$ and $3 - 2i$

4. $2 + 0 \cdot i$ and $-1 + 3i$

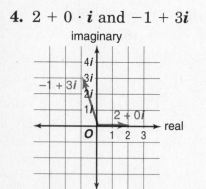

5. $3i$ and $-3 - i$

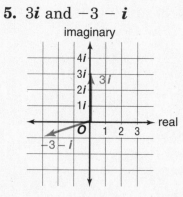

6. -3 and $2 - 2i$

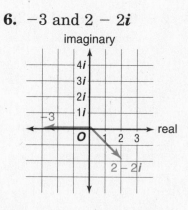

In each exercise, find the sum of the complex numbers in the exercise named. Then graph the sum in the grid for that exercise.

7. exercise 1 $3 + i$

8. exercise 2 $3 + 5i$

9. exercise 3 $2 + 2i$

10. exercise 4 $1 + 3i$

11. exercise 5 $-3 + 2i$

12. exercise 6 $-1 - 2i$

Algebra 2

Enrichment

Conjugates and Absolute Value

When studying complex numbers, it is often convenient to represent a complex number by a single variable. For example, we might let $z = x + yi$. We denote the conjugate of z by $\bar{z}$. Thus, $\bar{z} = x - yi$.

We can define the absolute value of a complex number as follows.

$$|z| = |x + yi| = \sqrt{x^2 + y^2}$$

There are many important relationships involving conjugates and absolute values of complex numbers.

Example: Show $|z|^2 = z\bar{z}$ for any complex number z.
Let $z = x + yi$. Then,
$$z\bar{z} = (x + yi)(x - yi)$$
$$= x^2 + y^2$$
$$= (\sqrt{x^2 + y^2})^2$$
$$= |z|^2$$

Example: Show $\dfrac{\bar{z}}{|z|^2}$ is the multiplicative inverse for any nonzero complex number z.

We know $|z|^2 = z\bar{z}$. If $z \neq 0$, then we have $z\left(\dfrac{\bar{z}}{|z|^2}\right) = 1$.

Thus, $\dfrac{\bar{z}}{|z|^2}$ is the multiplicative inverse of z.

For each of the following complex numbers, find the absolute value and multiplicative inverse.

1. $2i$

2. $-4 - 3i$

3. $12 - 5i$

4. $5 - 12i$

5. $1 + i$

6. $\sqrt{3} - i$

7. $\dfrac{\sqrt{3}}{3} + \dfrac{\sqrt{3}}{3}i$

8. $\dfrac{\sqrt{2}}{2} - \dfrac{\sqrt{2}}{2}i$

9. $\dfrac{1}{2} - \dfrac{\sqrt{3}}{2}i$

NAME_____ DATE _____

Enrichment

Conjugates and Absolute Value

When studying complex numbers, it is often convenient to represent a complex number by a single variable. For example, we might let $z = x + yi$. We denote the conjugate of z by $\bar{z}$. Thus, $\bar{z} = x - yi$.

We can define the absolute value of a complex number as follows.

$$|z| = |x + yi| = \sqrt{x^2 + y^2}$$

There are many important relationships involving conjugates and absolute values of complex numbers.

Example: Show $|z|^2 = z\bar{z}$ for any complex number z.
Let $z = x + yi$. Then,
$$z\bar{z} = (x + yi)(x - yi)$$
$$= x^2 + y^2$$
$$= (\sqrt{x^2 + y^2})^2$$
$$= |z|^2$$

Example: Show $\dfrac{\bar{z}}{|z|^2}$ is the multiplicative inverse for any nonzero complex number z.

We know $|z|^2 = z\bar{z}$. If $z \neq 0$, then we have $z\left(\dfrac{\bar{z}}{|z|^2}\right) = 1$.

Thus, $\dfrac{\bar{z}}{|z|^2}$ is the multiplicative inverse of z.

For each of the following complex numbers, find the absolute value and multiplicative inverse.

1. $2i$ $2; \dfrac{-i}{2}$

2. $-4 - 3i$ $5; \dfrac{-4 + 3i}{25}$

3. $12 - 5i$ $13; \dfrac{12 + 5i}{169}$

4. $5 - 12i$ $13; \dfrac{5 + 12i}{169}$

5. $1 + i$ $\sqrt{2}; \dfrac{1 - i}{2}$

6. $\sqrt{3} - i$ $2; \dfrac{\sqrt{3} + i}{4}$

7. $\dfrac{\sqrt{3}}{3} + \dfrac{\sqrt{3}}{3}i$
$\dfrac{\sqrt{6}}{3}; \dfrac{\sqrt{3} - i\sqrt{3}}{2}$

8. $\dfrac{\sqrt{2}}{2} - \dfrac{\sqrt{2}}{2}i$
$1; \dfrac{\sqrt{2}}{2} + \dfrac{\sqrt{2}}{2}i$

9. $\dfrac{1}{2} - \dfrac{\sqrt{3}}{2}i$
$1; \dfrac{1}{2} + \dfrac{\sqrt{3}}{3}i$

Algebra 2

Enrichment

Parametric Equations

Sometimes a graph is described by two equations rather than just one. For example, the coordinates (x, y) of a moving point are often described by two equations using the variable t for time.

$$x = t \qquad y = t^2$$

These are called **parametric equations** for the location of the point at time t. The variable t is the parameter.

Parametric equations are often used because an equation involving only x and y would be too complicated. Sometimes parameters provide the most straightforward description of the problem being solved.

Make a table of values and then sketch the graph of each set of parametric equations. The axes shown will help you choose appropriate values for t.

1. $x = t - 2$
   $y = 2t + 3$

2. $x = t$
   $y = t^2$

3. $x = t - 2$
   $y = t^2 - t + 1$

4. $x = t^2$
   $y = t$

5. $x = t^2 - 3t + 2$
   $y = t^2 + t - 1$

6. $x = t^3$
   $y = t^2$

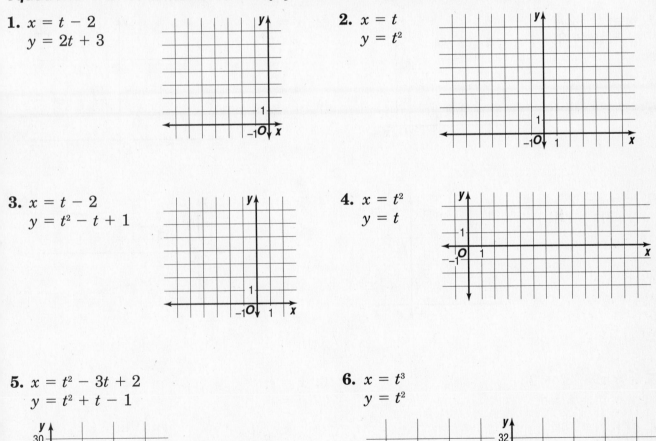

Enrichment

Parametric Equations

Sometimes a graph is described by two equations rather than just one. For example, the coordinates (x, y) of a moving point are often described by two equations using the variable t for time.

$$x = t \qquad y = t^2$$

These are called **parametric equations** for the location of the point at time t. The variable t is the parameter.

Parametric equations are often used because an equation involving only x and y would be too complicated. Sometimes parameters provide the most straightforward description of the problem being solved.

Make a table of values and then sketch the graph of each set of parametric equations. The axes shown will help you choose appropriate values for t.

1. $x = t - 2$
    $y = 2t + 3$

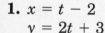

2. $x = t$
    $y = t^2$

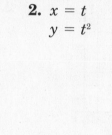

3. $x = t - 2$
    $y = t^2 - t + 1$

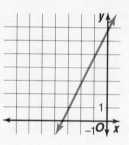

4. $x = t^2$
    $y = t$

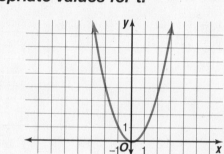

5. $x = t^2 - 3t + 2$
    $y = t^2 + t - 1$

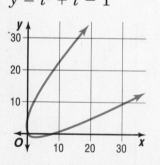

6. $x = t^3$
    $y = t^2$

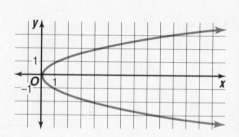

Enrichment

Quadratic Form

Consider two methods for solving the following equation.

$$(y - 2)^2 - 5(y - 2) + 6 = 0$$

One way to solve the equation is to simplify first, then use factoring.

$$y^2 - 4y + 4 - 5y + 10 + 6 = 0$$
$$y^2 - 9y + 20 = 0$$
$$(y - 4)(y - 5) = 0$$

Thus, the solution set is {4, 5}.

Another way to solve the equation is first to replace $y - 2$ by a single variable. This will produce an equation that is easier to solve than the original equation. Let $t = y - 2$ and then solve the new equation.

$$(y - 2)^2 - 5(y - 2) + 6 = 0$$
$$t^2 - 5t + 6 = 0$$
$$(t - 2)(t - 3) = 0$$

Thus, t is 2 or 3. Since $t = y - 2$, the solution set of the original equation is {4, 5}.

Solve each equation using two different methods.

1. $(z + 2)^2 + 8(z + 2) + 7 = 0$

2. $(3x - 1)^2 - (3x - 1) - 20 = 0$

3. $(2t + 1)^2 - 4(2t + 1) + 3 = 0$

4. $(y^2 - 1)^2 - (y^2 - 1) - 2 = 0$

5. $(a^2 - 2)^2 - 2(a^2 - 2) - 3 = 0$

6. $(1 + \sqrt{c})^2 + (1 + \sqrt{c}) - 6 = 0$

41

Enrichment

Quadratic Form

Consider two methods for solving the following equation.

$$(y - 2)^2 - 5(y - 2) + 6 = 0$$

One way to solve the equation is to simplify first, then use factoring.

$$y^2 - 4y + 4 - 5y + 10 + 6 = 0$$
$$y^2 - 9y + 20 = 0$$
$$(y - 4)(y - 5) = 0$$

Thus, the solution set is {4, 5}.

Another way to solve the equation is first to replace $y - 2$ by a single variable. This will produce an equation that is easier to solve than the original equation. Let $t = y - 2$ and then solve the new equation.

$$(y - 2)^2 - 5(y - 2) + 6 = 0$$
$$t^2 - 5t + 6 = 0$$
$$(t - 2)(t - 3) = 0$$

Thus, t is 2 or 3. Since $t = y - 2$, the solution set of the original equation is {4, 5}.

Solve each equation using two different methods.

1. $(z + 2)^2 + 8(z + 2) + 7 = 0$
   {−3, −9}

2. $(3x - 1)^2 - (3x - 1) - 20 = 0$
   {2, −1}

3. $(2t + 1)^2 - 4(2t + 1) + 3 = 0$
   {0, 1}

4. $(y^2 - 1)^2 - (y^2 - 1) - 2 = 0$
   {0, ±√3}

5. $(a^2 - 2)^2 - 2(a^2 - 2) - 3 = 0$
   {±1, ±√5}

6. $(1 + \sqrt{c})^2 + (1 + \sqrt{c}) - 6 = 0$
   {1}

NAME_____ DATE _____

Enrichment

Patterns with Differences and Sums of Squares

Some whole numbers can be written as the difference of two squares and some cannot. Formulas can be developed to describe the sets of numbers algebraically.

If possible, write each number as the difference of two squares. Look for patterns.

1. 0	**2.** 1	**3.** 2	**4.** 3
5. 4	**6.** 5	**7.** 6	**8.** 7
9. 8	**10.** 9	**11.** 10	**12.** 11
13. 12	**14.** 13	**15.** 14	**16.** 15

Even numbers can be written as 2n, where n is one of the numbers 0, 1, 2, 3, and so on. Odd numbers can be written 2n + 1. Use these expressions for these problems.

17. Show that any odd number can be written as the difference of two squares.

18. Show that the even numbers can be divided into two sets: those that can be written in the form $4n$ and those that can be written in the form $2 + 4n$.

19. Describe the even numbers that cannot be written as the difference of two squares.

20. Show that the other even numbers can be written as the difference of two squares.

Every whole number can be written as the sum of squares. It is never necessary to use more than four squares. Show that this is true for the whole numbers from 0 through 15 by writing each one as the sum of the least number of squares.

21. 0	**22.** 1	**23.** 2
24. 3	**25.** 4	**26.** 5
27. 6	**28.** 7	**29.** 8
30. 9	**31.** 10	**32.** 11
33. 12	**34.** 13	**35.** 14
36. 15		

Enrichment

Student Edition
Pages 346–352

Patterns with Differences and Sums of Squares

Some whole numbers can be written as the difference of two squares and some cannot. Formulas can be developed to describe the sets of numbers algebraically.

If possible, write each number as the difference of two squares. Look for patterns.

1. 0 $0^2 - 0^2$ 2. 1 $1^2 - 0^2$ 3. 2 cannot   4. 3 $2^2 - 1^2$

5. 4 $2^2 - 0^2$ 6. 5 $3^2 - 2^2$ 7. 6 cannot   8. 7 $4^2 - 3^2$

9. 8 $3^2 - 1^2$ 10. 9 $3^2 - 0^2$ 11. 10 cannot   12. 11 $6^2 - 5^2$

13. 12 $4^2 - 2^2$ 14. 13 $7^2 - 6^2$ 15. 14 cannot   16. 15 $4^2 - 1^2$

Even numbers can be written as 2n, where n is one of the numbers 0, 1, 2, 3, and so on. Odd numbers can be written 2n + 1. Use these expressions for these problems.

17. Show that any odd number can be written as the difference of two squares.
$2n + 1 = (n + 1)^2 - n^2$

18. Show that the even numbers can be divided into two sets: those that can be written in the form $4n$ and those that can be written in the form $2 + 4n$.
Find 4n for n = 0, 1, 2, and so on. You get {0, 4, 8, 12, ⋯}.
For 2 + 4n, you get {2, 6, 10, 12, ⋯}.
Together these sets include all even numbers.

19. Describe the even numbers that cannot be written as the difference of two squares.
$2 + 4n$, for $n = 0, 1, 2, 3, ⋯$

20. Show that the other even numbers can be written as the difference of two squares.
$4n = (n + 1)^2 - (n - 1)^2$

Every whole number can be written as the sum of squares. It is never necessary to use more than four squares. Show that this is true for the whole numbers from 0 through 15 by writing each one as the sum of the least number of squares.

21. 0 0^2 22. 1 1^2 23. 2 $1^2 + 1^2$

24. 3 $1^2 + 1^2 + 1^2$ 25. 4 2^2 26. 5 $1^2 + 2^2$

27. 6 $1^2 + 1^2 + 2^2$ 28. 7 $1^2 + 1^2 + 1^2 + 2^2$ 29. 8 $2^2 + 2^2$

30. 9 3^2 31. 10 $1^2 + 3^2$ 32. 11 $1^2 + 1^2 + 3^2$

33. 12 $1^2 + 1^2 + 1^2 + 3^2$ 34. 13 $2^2 + 3^2$ 35. 14 $1^2 + 2^2 + 3^2$

36. 15 $1^2 + 1^2 + 2^2 + 3^2$

      Algebra 2

NAME_____ DATE _____

Enrichment

The Golden Quadratic Equations

A **golden rectangle** has the property that its length can be written as $a + b$, where a is the width of the rectangle and

$$\frac{a + b}{a} = \frac{a}{b}.$$

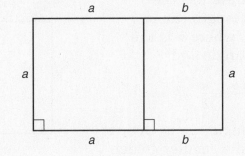

Any golden rectangle can be divided into a square and a smaller golden rectangle.

There are two quadratic equations that can be derived from the proportion used to define golden rectangles. These are sometimes called *golden quadratic equations*.

Solve each problem.

1. In the proportion for the golden rectangle, let a equal 1. Write the resulting quadratic equation and solve for b.

2. In the proportion, let b equal 1. Write the resulting quadratic equation and solve for a.

3. Describe the difference between the two golden quadratic equations you found in exercises 1 and 2.

4. Show that the positive solutions of the two equations in exercises 1 and 2 are reciprocals.

5. Use the Pythagorean theorem to find a radical expression for the diagonal of a golden rectangle with short side x and long side 1.

6. Find a radical expression for the diagonal of a golden rectangle with long side x and short side 1.

Algebra 2

Enrichment

The Golden Quadratic Equations

A **golden rectangle** has the property that its length can be written as $a + b$, where a is the width of the rectangle and

$$\frac{a+b}{a} = \frac{a}{b}.$$

Any golden rectangle can be divided into a square and a smaller golden rectangle.

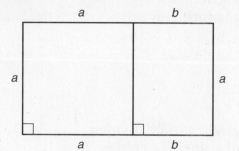

There are two quadratic equations that can be derived from the proportion used to define golden rectangles. These are sometimes called *golden quadratic equations*.

Solve each problem.

1. In the proportion for the golden rectangle, let a equal 1. Write the resulting quadratic equation and solve for b.
$$b^2 + b - 1 = 0$$

$$b = \frac{-1 + \sqrt{5}}{2}$$

2. In the proportion, let b equal 1. Write the resulting quadratic equation and solve for a.
$$a^2 - a - 1 = 0$$

$$a = \frac{1 + \sqrt{5}}{2}$$

3. Describe the difference between the two golden quadratic equations you found in exercises 1 and 2.
The signs of the first-degree terms are opposite.

4. Show that the positive solutions of the two equations in exercises 1 and 2 are reciprocals.

$$\left(\frac{-1 + \sqrt{5}}{2}\right)\left(\frac{1 + \sqrt{5}}{2}\right) =$$

$$\frac{-(1^2) + (\sqrt{5})^2}{4} = \frac{-1 + 5}{4} = 1$$

5. Use the Pythagorean theorem to find a radical expression for the diagonal of a golden rectangle with short side x and long side 1.

$$d = \frac{\sqrt{10 - 2\sqrt{5}}}{2}$$

6. Find a radical expression for the diagonal of a golden rectangle with long side x and short side 1.

$$d = \frac{\sqrt{10 + 2\sqrt{5}}}{2}$$

Enrichment

Euler's Formula for Prime Numbers

Many mathematicians have searched for a formula that would generate prime numbers. One such formula was proposed by Euler and uses a quadratic polynomial:

$$x^2 + x + 41.$$

Find the values of $x^2 + x + 41$ for the given values of x. State whether each value of the polynomial is or is not a prime number.

1. $x = 0$

2. $x = 1$

3. $x = 2$

4. $x = 3$

5. $x = 4$

6. $x = 5$

7. $x = 6$

8. $x = 17$

9. $x = 28$

10. $x = 29$

11. $x = 30$

12. $x = 35$

13. Does the formula produce all prime numbers greater than 40? Give examples in your answer.

14. Euler's formula produces primes for many values of x, but it does not work for all of them. Find the first value of x for which the formula fails. (*Hint:* Try multiples of ten.)

NAME_____ DATE _____

Enrichment

Student Edition
Pages 359–364

Euler's Formula for Prime Numbers

Many mathematicians have searched for a formula that would generate prime numbers. One such formula was proposed by Euler and uses a quadratic polynomial:

$$x^2 + x + 41.$$

Find the values of $x^2 + x + 41$ for the given values of x. State whether each value of the polynomial is or is not a prime number.

1. $x = 0$
41, prime

2. $x = 1$
43, prime

3. $x = 2$
47, prime

4. $x = 3$
53, prime

5. $x = 4$
61, prime

6. $x = 5$
71, prime

7. $x = 6$
83, prime

8. $x = 17$
347, prime

9. $x = 28$
853, prime

10. $x = 29$
911, prime

11. $x = 30$
971, prime

12. $x = 35$
1301, prime

13. Does the formula produce all prime numbers greater than 40? Give examples in your answer.
No. Among the primes omitted are 59, 67, 73, 79, 89, 101, 103, 107, 109, and 127.

14. Euler's formula produces primes for many values of x, but it does not work for all of them. Find the first value of x for which the formula fails. (*Hint:* Try multiples of ten.)
$x = 40$ gives 1681, which equals 41^2.

Algebra 2

Enrichment

Finding the Axis of Symmetry of a Parabola

As you know, if $f(x) = ax^2 + bx + c$ is a quadratic function, the values of x that make $f(x)$ equal to zero are

$$\frac{-b + \sqrt{b^2 - 4ac}}{2a} \text{ and } \frac{-b - \sqrt{b^2 - 4ac}}{2a}.$$

The average of these two number values is $-\frac{b}{2a}$. The function $f(x)$ has its maximum or minimum value when $x = -\frac{b}{2a}$. Since the axis of symmetry of the graph of $f(x)$ passes through the point where the maximum or minimum occurs, the axis of symmetry has the equation $x = -\frac{b}{2a}$.

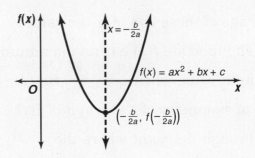

Example: Find the vertex and axis of symmetry for $f(x) = 5x^2 + 10x - 7.$

Use $x = -\frac{b}{2a}.$

$x = -\frac{10}{2(5)} = -1$ The x-coordinate of the vertex is -1.

Substitute $x = -1$ in $f(x) = 5x^2 + 10x - 7.$

$f(-1) = 5(-1)^2 + 10(-1) - 7 = -12$

The vertex is $(-1, -12).$

The axis of symmetry is $x = -\frac{b}{2a}$, or $x = -1.$

Find the vertex and axis of symmetry for the graph of each function using $x = -\frac{b}{2a}.$

1. $f(x) = x^2 - 4x - 8$

2. $g(x) = -4x^2 - 8x + 3$

3. $y = -x^2 + 8x + 3$

4. $f(x) = 2x^2 + 6x + 5$

5. $A(x) = x^2 + 12x + 36$

6. $k(x) = -2x^2 + 2x - 6$

Enrichment

Finding the Axis of Symmetry of a Parabola

As you know, if $f(x) = ax^2 + bx + c$ is a
quadratic function, the values of x that
make $f(x)$ equal to zero are

$$\frac{-b + \sqrt{b^2 - 4ac}}{2a} \quad \text{and} \quad \frac{-b - \sqrt{b^2 - 4ac}}{2a}.$$

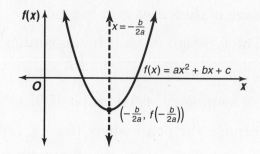

The average of these two number values
is $-\dfrac{b}{2a}$. The function $f(x)$ has its maximum
or minimum value when $x = -\dfrac{b}{2a}$. Since
the axis of symmetry of the graph of $f(x)$
passes through the point where the
maximum or minimum occurs, the axis
of symmetry has the equation $x = -\dfrac{b}{2a}$.

Example: Find the vertex and axis of symmetry for
$f(x) = 5x^2 + 10x - 7$.

Use $x = -\dfrac{b}{2a}$.

$x = -\dfrac{10}{2(5)} = -1$ The x-coordinate of the vertex is -1.

Substitute $x = -1$ in $f(x) = 5x^2 + 10x - 7$.

$f(-1) = 5(-1)^2 + 10(-1) - 7 = -12$

The vertex is $(-1, -12)$.

The axis of symmetry is $x = -\dfrac{b}{2a}$, or $x = -1$.

**Find the vertex and axis of symmetry for the graph of each
function using $x = -\dfrac{b}{2a}$.**

1. $f(x) = x^2 - 4x - 8$ **(2, −12); $x = 2$**

2. $g(x) = -4x^2 - 8x + 3$ **(−1, 7); $x = -1$**

3. $y = -x^2 + 8x + 3$ **(4, 19); $x = 4$**

4. $f(x) = 2x^2 + 6x + 5$ $\left(-\dfrac{3}{2}, \dfrac{1}{2}\right); x = -\dfrac{3}{2}$

5. $A(x) = x^2 + 12x + 36$ **(−6, 0); $x = -6$**

6. $k(x) = -2x^2 + 2x - 6$ $\left(\dfrac{1}{2}, -5\dfrac{1}{2}\right); x = \dfrac{1}{2}$

Quadratic Relationships in Triangles

The **triangle inequality** states that the
sum of any two sides of a triangle is
greater than the length of the third side.
For the triangle in the diagram, the sides
measure 1, r, and r^2.

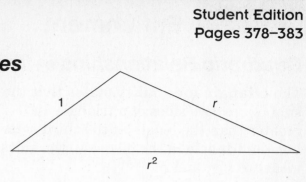

Solve each problem.

1. Write an equality comparing the sum of
the two shorter sides to the longest side.

2. Solve the inequality from problem 1
for r.

3. Compare the sum of the two longer
sides to the shortest side.

4. Solve the inequality in problem 3 for r.

5. What possible values can r have in the
triangle?

6. A golden rectangle has sides r and 1
that satisfy the proportion $r : 1 = (r + 1) : r$. Solve for r and relate this
answer to the results of problem 5.

*Look for the so-called golden ratio, $\dfrac{1 + \sqrt{5}}{2}$, to appear as you
solve the following problems. Triangles ABC and A'B'C' are both
isosceles, with AY = XB and A'Y' = X'B'.*

7. Write a proportion showing that the
sides of triangles ABC and ACX form
equal ratios. Use b for the length of the
long side of triangle ABC.

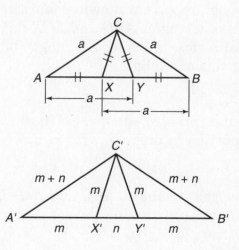

8. Let the ratio $b{:}a$ equal r. Solve the
proportion in problem 7 for r.

9. Show that triangles ABC and $A'B'C'$
are similar by finding the ratio r' in
the triangle $A'B'C'$.

Enrichment

Quadratic Relationships in Triangles

The **triangle inequality** states that the sum of any two sides of a triangle is greater than the length of the third side. For the triangle in the diagram, the sides measure 1, r, and r^2.

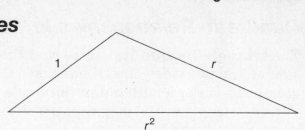

Solve each problem.

1. Write an equality comparing the sum of the two shorter sides to the longest side.
   $$1 + r > r^2$$

2. Solve the inequality from problem 1 for r.
   $$r < \frac{1 + \sqrt{5}}{2}$$

3. Compare the sum of the two longer sides to the shortest side.
   $$r^2 + r > 1$$

4. Solve the inequality in problem 3 for r.
   $$r > \frac{-1 + \sqrt{5}}{2}$$

5. What possible values can r have in the triangle?
   $$\frac{-1 + \sqrt{5}}{2} < r < \frac{1 + \sqrt{5}}{2}$$

6. A golden rectangle has sides r and 1 that satisfy the proportion $r : 1 = (r + 1) : r$. Solve for r and relate this answer to the results of problem 5.

   $r = \dfrac{1 + \sqrt{5}}{2}$; **the range of values**

   for r in the triangle lies

   between $\dfrac{1 + \sqrt{5}}{2}$ **and** $\dfrac{-1 + \sqrt{5}}{2}$.

Look for the so-called golden ratio, $\dfrac{1 + \sqrt{5}}{2}$, to appear as you solve the following problems. Triangles ABC and A'B'C' are both isosceles, with AY = XB and A'Y' = X'B'.

7. Write a proportion showing that the sides of triangles ABC and ACX form equal ratios. Use b for the length of the long side of triangle ABC.
   $$\frac{a}{b} = \frac{b - a}{a}$$

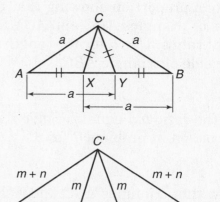

8. Let the ratio $b{:}a$ equal r. Solve the proportion in problem 7 for r.
   $$\frac{a}{b} = \frac{b}{a} - 1, \text{ so } \frac{1}{r} = r - 1; r = \frac{1 + \sqrt{5}}{2}$$

9. Show that triangles ABC and $A'B'C'$ are similar by finding the ratio r' in the triangle $A'B'C'$.

   $\dfrac{m + n}{2m + n} = \dfrac{m}{m + n}$; for $r' = \dfrac{2m + n}{m + n}$,

   $\dfrac{m + n}{2m + n} = \dfrac{2m + n}{m + n} - \dfrac{m + n}{m + n}$ and $\dfrac{1}{r'} = r' - 1$.

   So, $r = r'$ and the figures are similar.

Algebra 2

Enrichment

Correlation

There is a useful number, called the **correlation coefficient,** that gives a measure of how well a group of data items is clustered around a line. If the values of y are almost in direct proportion to the values of x, then the data points in a graph will cluster around a line and the correlation coefficient, r, will be close to 1. If the values of y are inversely proportional to x and closely bunched around a line, the correlation coefficient r will be close to -1. If there is no close correlation, $r = 0$.

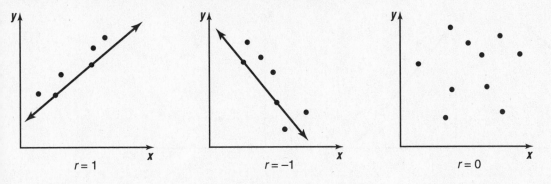

$r = 1$ $r = -1$ $r = 0$

The correlation coefficient is calculated as follows.

$$S_{xx} = \Sigma x^2 - \frac{(\Sigma x)^2}{n}$$

Note: Σx^2 is shorthand for $\sum_{i=1}^{n} x_i^2$.

$$r = \frac{S_{xy}}{\sqrt{S_{xx} \cdot S_{yy}}}$$

$$S_{yy} = \Sigma y^2 - \frac{(\Sigma y)^2}{n}$$

$$S_{xy} = \Sigma xy - \frac{\Sigma x \Sigma y}{n}$$

Use the formula to find the correlation coefficient for the following students scores in math and English.

1.

Student	Math (x)	English (y)
1	82	79
2	53	50
3	61	87
4	74	96
5	51	73
6	51	73

2.

Student	Math (x)	English (y)
1	92	70
2	86	80
3	43	40
4	60	72
5	75	60
6	80	92

Enrichment

Correlation

There is a useful number, called the **correlation coefficient,** that gives a measure of how well a group of data items is clustered around a line. If the values of y are almost in direct proportion to the values of x, then the data points in a graph will cluster around a line and the correlation coefficient, r, will be close to 1. If the values of y are inversely proportional to x and closely bunched around a line, the correlation coefficient r will be close to -1. If there is no close correlation, $r = 0$.

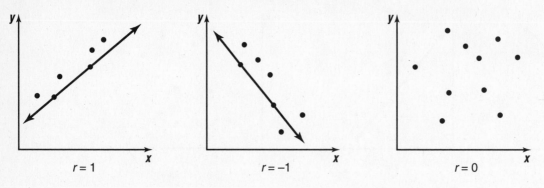

The correlation coefficient is calculated as follows.

$$S_{xx} = \Sigma x^2 - \frac{(\Sigma x)^2}{n}$$

Note: Σx^2 is shorthand for $\sum_{i=1}^{n} x_i^2$.

$$r = \frac{S_{xy}}{\sqrt{S_{xx} \cdot S_{yy}}} \qquad S_{yy} = \Sigma y^2 - \frac{(\Sigma y)^2}{n}$$

$$S_{xy} = \Sigma xy - \frac{\Sigma x \Sigma y}{n}$$

Use the formula to find the correlation coefficient for the following students scores in math and English.

1.

Student	Math (x)	English (y)
1	82	79
2	53	50
3	61	87
4	74	96
5	51	73
6	51	73

0.572

2.

Student	Math (x)	English (y)
1	92	70
2	86	80
3	43	40
4	60	72
5	75	60
6	80	92

0.703

Algebra 2

Enrichment

Shapes of Distribution Curves

Graphs of frequency distributions can be described as either symmetric or skewed.

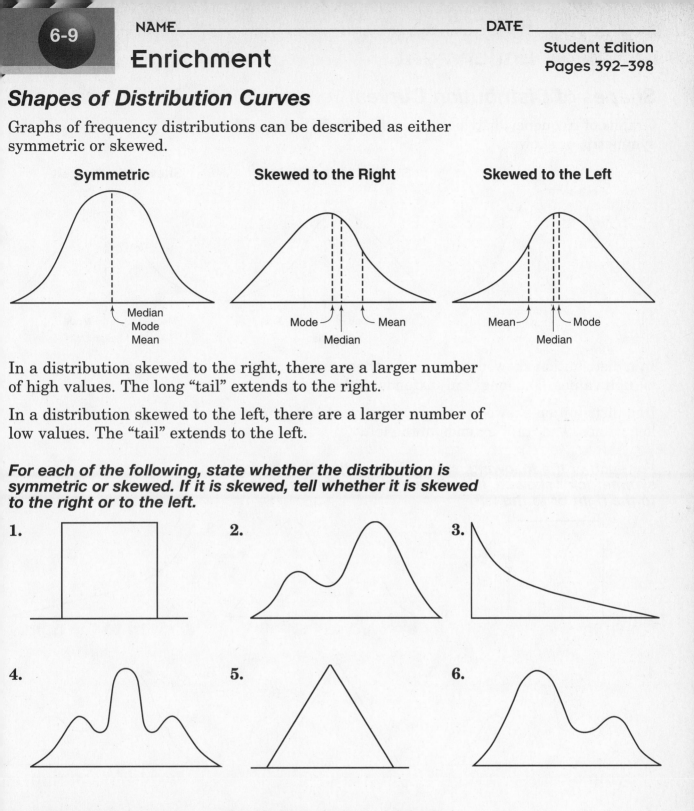

In a distribution skewed to the right, there are a larger number of high values. The long "tail" extends to the right.

In a distribution skewed to the left, there are a larger number of low values. The "tail" extends to the left.

For each of the following, state whether the distribution is symmetric or skewed. If it is skewed, tell whether it is skewed to the right or to the left.

1.

2.

3.

4.

5.

6.

A vertical line above the median divides the area under a frequency curve in half.

7. Where is the median in a symmetric distribution?

8. Where is the median in a skewed distribution?

Enrichment

Shapes of Distribution Curves

Graphs of frequency distributions can be described as either symmetric or skewed.

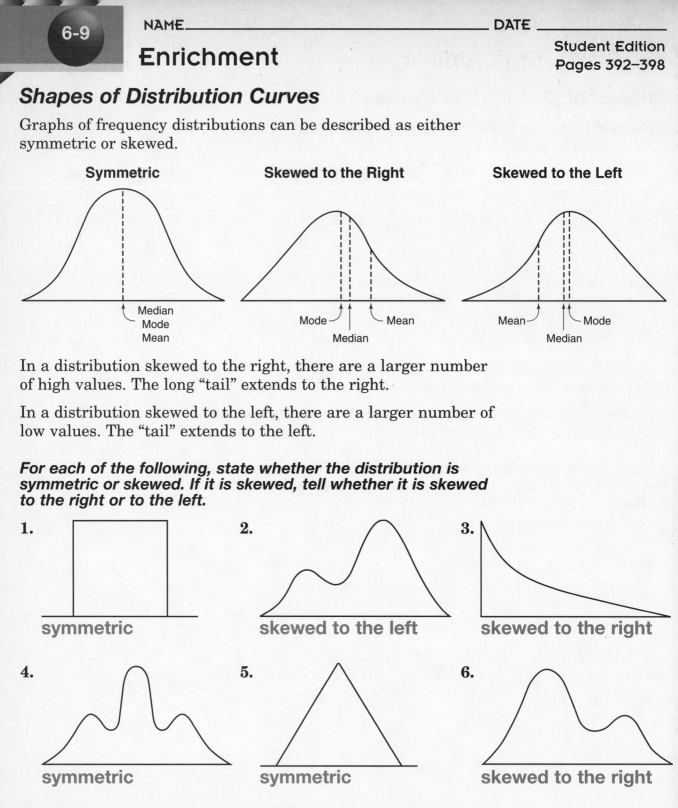

Symmetric

Median
Mode
Mean

Skewed to the Right

Mode ⌐ ⌐ Mean
Median

Skewed to the Left

Mean ⌐ ⌐ Mode
Median

In a distribution skewed to the right, there are a larger number of high values. The long "tail" extends to the right.

In a distribution skewed to the left, there are a larger number of low values. The "tail" extends to the left.

For each of the following, state whether the distribution is symmetric or skewed. If it is skewed, tell whether it is skewed to the right or to the left.

1.

symmetric

2.

skewed to the left

3.

skewed to the right

4.

symmetric

5.

symmetric

6.

skewed to the right

A vertical line above the median divides the area under a frequency curve in half.

7. Where is the median in a symmetric distribution?
in the middle of the range; It is the same as the mean.

8. Where is the median in a skewed distribution?
to the left of the middle if skewed to the right; to the right of the middle if skewed to the left

Enrichment

Reading Algebra

If two mathematical problems have basic structural
similarities, they are said to be **analogous.** Using analogies
is one way of discovering and proving new theorems.

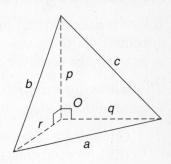

The following numbered sentences discuss a three-
dimensional analogy to the Pythagorean theorem.

01 Consider a tetrahedron with three perpendicular faces
    that meet at vertex O.
02 Suppose you want to know how the areas A, B, and C of
    the three faces that meet at vertex O are related to the
    area D of the face opposite vertex O.
03 It is natural to expect a formula analogous to the
    Pythagorean theorem $z^2 = x^2 + y^2$, which is true for a
    similar situation in two dimensions.
04 To explore the three-dimensional case, you might guess
    a formula and then try to prove it.
05 Two reasonable guesses are $D^3 = A^3 + B^3 + C^3$ and
    $D^2 = A^2 + B^2 + C^2$.

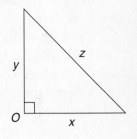

Refer to the numbered sentences to answer the questions.

1. Use sentence 01 and the top diagram. The prefix *tetra-* means
    four. Write an informal definition of tetrahedron.

2. Use sentence 02 and the top diagram. What are the lengths of
    the sides of each face of the tetrahedron?

3. Rewrite sentence 01 to state a two-dimensional analogue.

4. Refer to the top diagram and write expressions for the areas
    A, B, and C mentioned in sentence 02.

5. To explore the three-dimensional case, you might begin by
    expressing a, b, and c in terms of p, q, and r. Use the
    Pythagorean theorem to do this.

6. Which guess in sentence 05 seems more likely? Justify your
    answer.

Enrichment

Reading Algebra

If two mathematical problems have basic structural
similarities, they are said to be **analogous.** Using analogies
is one way of discovering and proving new theorems.

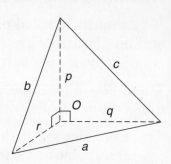

The following numbered sentences discuss a three-
dimensional analogy to the Pythagorean theorem.

01 Consider a tetrahedron with three perpendicular faces
    that meet at vertex O.

02 Suppose you want to know how the areas A, B, and C of
    the three faces that meet at vertex O are related to the
    area D of the face opposite vertex O.

03 It is natural to expect a formula analogous to the
    Pythagorean theorem $z^2 = x^2 + y^2$, which is true for a
    similar situation in two dimensions.

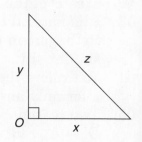

04 To explore the three-dimensional case, you might guess
    a formula and then try to prove it.

05 Two reasonable guesses are $D^3 = A^3 + B^3 + C^3$ and
    $D^2 = A^2 + B^2 + C^2$.

Refer to the numbered sentences to answer the questions.

1. Use sentence 01 and the top diagram. The prefix *tetra-* means
   four. Write an informal definition of tetrahedron.
   a three-dimensional figure with four faces

2. Use sentence 02 and the top diagram. What are the lengths of
   the sides of each face of the tetrahedron?
   a, b, and c; a, q, and r; b, p, and r; c, p, and q

3. Rewrite sentence 01 to state a two-dimensional analogue.
   **Consider a triangle with two perpendicular sides
   that meet at vertex C.**

4. Refer to the top diagram and write expressions for the areas
   A, B, and C mentioned in sentence 02.

   Possible answer: $A = \frac{1}{2}pr$, $B = \frac{1}{2}pq$, $C = \frac{1}{2}rq$

5. To explore the three-dimensional case, you might begin by
   expressing a, b, and c in terms of p, q, and r. Use the
   Pythagorean theorem to do this.
   $a^2 = q^2 + r^2$, $b^2 = r^2 + p^2$, $c^2 = p^2 + q^2$

6. Which guess in sentence 05 seems more likely? Justify your
   answer. **See students' explanations.**

Enrichment

Tangents to Parabolas

A line that intersects a parabola in exactly one point without crossing the curve is a **tangent** to the parabola. The point where a tangent line touches a parabola is the **point of tangency.** The line perpendicular to a tangent to a parabola at the point of tangency is called the **normal** to the parabola at that point. In the diagram, line l is tangent to the parabola that is the graph of $y = x^2$ at $\left(\frac{3}{2}, \frac{9}{4}\right)$. The x-axis is tangent to the parabola at O, and the y-axis is the normal to the parabola at O.

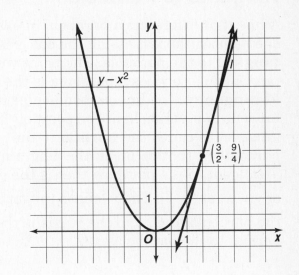

Solve each problem.

1. Find an equation for line l in the diagram. *Hint:* A nonvertical line with an equation of the form $y = mx + b$ will be tangent to the graph of $y = x^2$ at $\left(\frac{3}{2}, \frac{9}{4}\right)$ if and only if $\left(\frac{3}{2}, \frac{9}{4}\right)$ is the only pair of numbers that satisfies both $y = x^2$ and $y = mx + b$.

2. If a is any real number, then (a, a^2) belongs to the graph of $y = x^2$. Express m and b in terms of a to find an equation of the form $y = mx + b$ for the line that is tangent to the graph of $y = x^2$ at (a, a^2).

3. Find an equation for the normal to the graph of $y = x^2$ at $\left(\frac{3}{2}, \frac{9}{4}\right)$.

4. If a is a nonzero real number, find an equation for the normal to the graph of $y = x^2$ at (a, a^2).

NAME_____ DATE _____

Enrichment

Student Edition
Pages 415–422

Tangents to Parabolas

A line that intersects a parabola in exactly
one point without crossing the curve is a
tangent to the parabola. The point where a
tangent line touches a parabola is the **point
of tangency.** The line perpendicular to a
tangent to a parabola at the point of
tangency is called the **normal** to the
parabola at that point. In the diagram, line l
is tangent to the parabola that is the graph
of $y = x^2$ at $\left(\frac{3}{2}, \frac{9}{4}\right)$. The x-axis is tangent to
the parabola at O, and the y-axis is the
normal to the parabola at O.

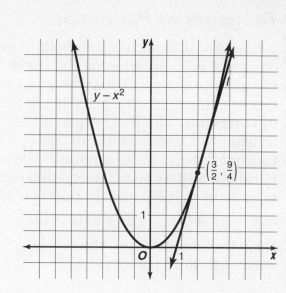

Solve each problem.

1. Find an equation for line l in the diagram. *Hint:* A nonvertical
   line with an equation of the form $y = mx + b$ will be tangent
   to the graph of $y = x^2$ at $\left(\frac{3}{2}, \frac{9}{4}\right)$ if and only if $\left(\frac{3}{2}, \frac{9}{4}\right)$ is the only
   pair of numbers that satisfies both $y = x^2$ and $y = mx + b$.
   $m = 3, b = -\frac{9}{4}, y = 3x - \frac{9}{4}$

2. If a is any real number, then (a, a^2) belongs to the graph of
   $y = x^2$. Express m and b in terms of a to find an equation of
   the form $y = mx + b$ for the line that is tangent to the graph
   of $y = x^2$ at (a, a^2).
   $m = 2a, b = a^2, y = (2a)x + (-a^2)$ or $y = 2ax - a^2$

3. Find an equation for the normal to the graph of $y = x^2$ at
   $\left(\frac{3}{2}, \frac{9}{4}\right)$.
   $y = -\frac{1}{3}x + \frac{11}{4}$

4. If a is a nonzero real number, find an equation for the normal
   to the graph of $y = x^2$ at (a, a^2).
   $y = \left(-\frac{1}{2a}\right)x + \left(a^2 + \frac{1}{2}\right)$

Enrichment

Tangents to Circles

A line that intersects a circle in exactly one point is a **tangent** to the circle. In the diagram, line l is tangent to the circle with equation $x^2 + y^2 = 25$ at the point whose coordinates are (3, 4).

A line is tangent to a circle at a point P on the circle if and only if the line is perpendicular to the radius from the center of the circle to point P. This fact enables you to find an equation of the tangent to a circle at a point P if you know an equation for the circle and the coordinates of P.

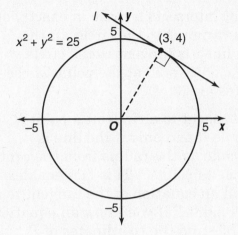

Use the diagram above to solve each problem.

1. What is the slope of the radius to the point with coordinates (3, 4)? What is the slope of the tangent to that point?

2. Find an equation of the line l that is tangent to the circle at (3, 4).

3. If k is a real number between -5 and 5, how many points on the circle have x-coordinate k? State the coordinates of these points in terms of k.

4. Describe how you can find equations for the tangents to the points you named for Exercise 3.

5. Find an equation for the tangent at $(-3, 4)$.

Enrichment

Tangents to Circles

A line that intersects a circle in exactly one point is a **tangent** to the circle. In the diagram, line l is tangent to the circle with equation $x^2 + y^2 = 25$ at the point whose coordinates are (3, 4).

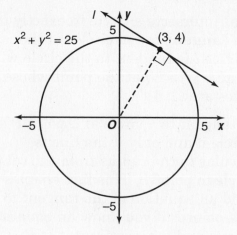

A line is tangent to a circle at a point P on the circle if and only if the line is perpendicular to the radius from the center of the circle to point P. This fact enables you to find an equation of the tangent to a circle at a point P if you know an equation for the circle and the coordinates of P.

Use the diagram above to solve each problem.

1. What is the slope of the radius to the point with coordinates (3, 4)? What is the slope of the tangent to that point? $\dfrac{4}{3}$, $-\dfrac{3}{4}$

2. Find an equation of the line l that is tangent to the circle at (3, 4). $y = -\dfrac{3}{4}x + \dfrac{25}{4}$

3. If k is a real number between -5 and 5, how many points on the circle have x-coordinate k? State the coordinates of these points in terms of k. two, $\left(k, \pm \sqrt{25 - k^2}\right)$

4. Describe how you can find equations for the tangents to the points you named for Exercise 3.
   Use the coordinates of (0, 0) and of one of the given points. Find the slope of the radius to that point. Use the slope of the radius to find what the slope of the tangent must be. Use the slope of the tangent and the coordinates of the point on the circle to find an equation for the tangent.

5. Find an equation for the tangent at $(-3, 4)$.
   $y = \dfrac{3}{4}x + \dfrac{25}{x}$

Superellipses

The circle and the ellipse are members of an interesting family of curves that were first studied by the French physicist and mathematician Gabriel Lamé (1795–1870). The general equation for the family is $\left|\frac{x}{a}\right|^n + \left|\frac{y}{b}\right|^n = 1$, with $a \neq 0$, $b \neq 0$, and $n > 0$. For even values of n greater than 2, the curves are called **superellipses.**

1. Consider two curves that are *not* superellipses. Graph each equation on the grid at the right. State the type of curve produced each time.

   a. $\left|\frac{x}{2}\right|^2 + \left|\frac{y}{2}\right|^2 = 1$

   b. $\left|\frac{x}{3}\right|^2 + \left|\frac{y}{2}\right|^2 = 1$

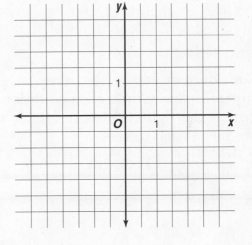

2. In each of the following cases you are given values of a, b, and n to use in the general equation. Write the resulting equation. Then graph. Sketch each graph on the grid at the right.

   a. $a = 2$, $b = 3$, $n = 4$
   b. $a = 2$, $b = 3$, $n = 6$
   c. $a = 2$, $b = 3$, $n = 8$

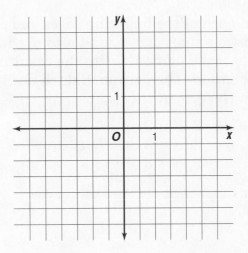

3. What shape will the graph of $\left|\frac{x}{2}\right|^n + \left|\frac{y}{3}\right|^n$ approximate for greater and greater even, whole-number values of n?

NAME_____ DATE _____

Enrichment

Superellipses

The circle and the ellipse are members of an interesting family of curves that were first studied by the French physicist and mathematician Gabriel Lamé (1795–1870). The general equation for the family is $\left|\dfrac{x}{a}\right|^n + \left|\dfrac{y}{b}\right|^n = 1$, with $a \neq 0$, $b \neq 0$, and $n > 0$. For even values of n greater than 2, the curves are called **superellipses**.

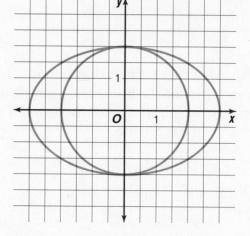

1. Consider two curves that are *not* superellipses. Graph each equation on the grid at the right. State the type of curve produced each time.

   a. $\left|\dfrac{x}{2}\right|^2 + \left|\dfrac{y}{2}\right|^2 = 1$ **circle**

   b. $\left|\dfrac{x}{3}\right|^2 + \left|\dfrac{y}{2}\right|^2 = 1$ **ellipse**

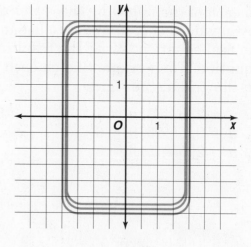

2. In each of the following cases you are given values of a, b, and n to use in the general equation. Write the resulting equation. Then graph. Sketch each graph on the grid at the right.

   a. $a = 2$, $b = 3$, $n = 4$ **See**
   b. $a = 2$, $b = 3$, $n = 6$ **students'**
   c. $a = 2$, $b = 3$, $n = 8$ **graphs.**

3. What shape will the graph of $\left|\dfrac{x}{2}\right|^n + \left|\dfrac{y}{3}\right|^n$ approximate for greater and greater even, whole-number values of n?
   a rectangle that is 6 units long and 4 units wide, centered at the origin

Graphing with Addition of y-Coordinates

Equations of parabolas, ellipses, and hyperbolas that are "tipped" with respect to the x- and y-axes are more difficult to graph than the equations you have been studying.

Often, however, you can use the graphs of two simpler equations to graph a more complicated equation. For example, the graph of the ellipse in the diagram at the right is obtained by adding the y-coordinate of each point on the circle and the y-coordinate of the corresponding point of the line.

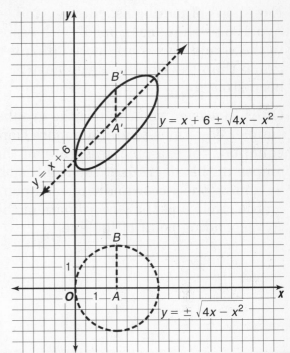

$y = x + 6 \pm \sqrt{4x - x^2}$

$y = x + 6$

$y = \pm \sqrt{4x - x^2}$

Graph each equation. State the type of curve for each graph.

1. $y = 6 - x \pm \sqrt{4 - x^2}$

2. $y = x \pm \sqrt{x}$

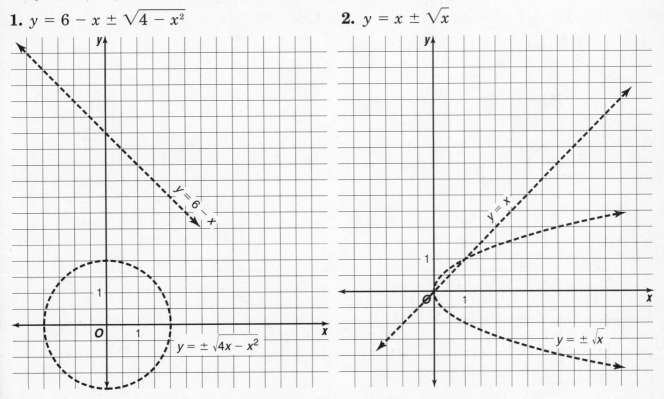

$y = 6 - x$

$y = \pm \sqrt{4x - x^2}$

$y = x$

$y = \pm \sqrt{x}$

Use a separate sheet of graph paper to graph these equations. State the type of curve for each graph.

3. $y = 2x \pm \sqrt{7 + 6x - x^2}$

4. $y = -2x \pm \sqrt{-2x}$

Enrichment

Graphing with Addition of y-Coordinates

Equations of parabolas, ellipses, and hyperbolas that are "tipped" with respect to the x- and y-axes are more difficult to graph than the equations you have been studying.

Often, however, you can use the graphs of two simpler equations to graph a more complicated equation. For example, the graph of the ellipse in the diagram at the right is obtained by adding the y-coordinate of each point on the circle and the y-coordinate of the corresponding point of the line.

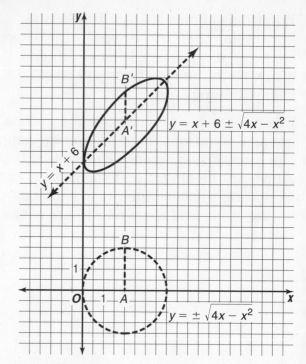

$y = x + 6 \pm \sqrt{4x - x^2}$

$y = x + 6$

$y = \pm \sqrt{4x - x^2}$

Graph each equation. State the type of curve for each graph.

1. $y = 6 - x \pm \sqrt{4 - x^2}$ **ellipse**

2. $y = x \pm \sqrt{x}$ **parabola**

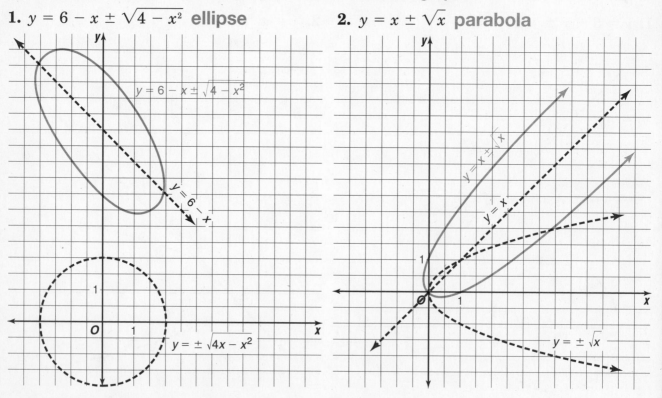

$y = 6 - x \pm \sqrt{4 - x^2}$

$y = 6 - x$

$y = \pm \sqrt{4x - x^2}$

$y = x \pm \sqrt{x}$

$y = x$

$y = \pm \sqrt{x}$

Use a separate sheet of graph paper to graph these equations. State the type of curve for each graph.

3. $y = 2x \pm \sqrt{7 + 6x - x^2}$ **ellipse**
See students' graphs.

4. $y = -2x \pm \sqrt{-2x}$ **parabola**
See students' graphs.

Algebra 2

Enrichment

Loci

A *locus* (plural, *loci*) is the set of all points, and only those points, that satisfy a given set of conditions. In geometry, figures often are defined as loci. For example, a circle is the locus of points of a plane that are a given distance from a given point. The definition leads naturally to an equation whose graph is the curve described.

Example: Write an equation of the locus of points that are the same distance from $(3, 4)$ and $y = -4$.

Recognizing that the locus is a parabola with focus $(3, 4)$ and directrix $y = -4$, you can find that $h = 3$, $k = 0$, and $a = 4$ where (h, k) is the vertex and 4 units is the distance from the vertex to both the focus and directrix.

Thus, an equation for the parabola is $y = \frac{1}{16}(x - 3)^2$.

The problem also may be approached analytically as follows:

Let (x, y) be a point of the locus.

The distance from $(3, 4)$ to (x, y) = the distance from $y = -4$ to (x, y).

$$\sqrt{(x - 3)^2 + (y - 4)^2} = \sqrt{(x - x)^2 + (y - (-4))^2}$$

$$(x - 3)^2 + y^2 - 8y + 16 = y^2 + 8y + 16$$

$$(x - 3)^2 = 16y$$

$$\frac{1}{16}(x - 3)^2 = y$$

State what type of curve each locus is. Then write an equation for the locus.

1. All points that are the same distance from $(0, 5)$ and $(4, 5)$.

2. All points that are 4 units from the origin.

3. All points that are the same distance from $(-2, -1)$ and $x = 2$.

4. The locus of points such that the sum of the distances from $(-2, 0)$ and $(2, 0)$ is 6.

5. The locus of points such that the absolute value of the difference of the distances from $(-3, 0)$ and $(3, 0)$ is 2.

Enrichment

Loci

A *locus* (plural, *loci*) is the set of all points, and only those points, that satisfy a given set of conditions. In geometry, figures often are defined as loci. For example, a circle is the locus of points of a plane that are a given distance from a given point. The definition leads naturally to an equation whose graph is the curve described.

Example: Write an equation of the locus of points that are the same distance from (3, 4) and $y = -4$.

Recognizing that the locus is a parabola with focus (3, 4) and directrix $y = -4$, you can find that $h = 3$, $k = 0$, and $a = 4$ where (h, k) is the vertex and 4 units is the distance from the vertex to both the focus and directrix.

Thus, an equation for the parabola is $y = \frac{1}{16}(x - 3)^2$.

The problem also may be approached analytically as follows:

Let (x, y) be a point of the locus.

The distance from (3, 4) to (x, y) = the distance from $y = -4$ to (x, y).

$$\sqrt{(x - 3)^2 + (y - 4)^2} = \sqrt{(x - x)^2 + (y - (-4))^2}$$

$$(x - 3)^2 + y^2 - 8y + 16 = y^2 + 8y + 16$$

$$(x - 3)^2 = 16y$$

$$\frac{1}{16}(x - 3)^2 = y$$

State what type of curve each locus is. Then write an equation for the locus.

1. All points that are the same distance from (0, 5) and (4, 5). **line, $x = 2$**

2. All points that are 4 units from the origin. **circle, $x^2 + y^2 = 4$**

3. All points that are the same distance from $(-2, -1)$ and $x = 2$.
   parabola, $x = \frac{-1}{8}(y^2 + 2y + 1)$

4. The locus of points such that the sum of the distances from $(-2, 0)$ and (2, 0) is 6. **ellipse, $\frac{x^2}{9} + \frac{y^2}{5} = 1$**

5. The locus of points such that the absolute value of the difference of the distances from $(-3, 0)$ and (3, 0) is 2. **hyperbola, $\frac{x^2}{1} - \frac{y^2}{8} = 1$**

NAME_____ DATE _____

Enrichment

Graphing Quadratic Equations with xy-Terms

You can use a graphing calculator to examine graphs of quadratic equations that contain xy-terms.

Example: Use a graphing calculator to display the graph of $x^2 + xy + y^2 = 4$.

Solve the equation for y in terms of x by using the quadratic formula.

$$y^2 + xy + (x^2 - 4) = 0$$

To use the formula, let $a = 1$, $b = x$, and $c = (x^2 - 4)$.

$$y = \frac{-x \pm \sqrt{x^2 - 4(1)(x^2 - 4)}}{2}$$

$$y = \frac{-x \pm \sqrt{16 - 3x^2}}{2}$$

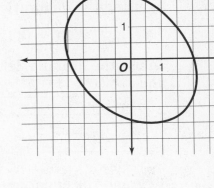

To graph the equation on the graphing calculator, enter the two equations:

$$y = \frac{-x + \sqrt{16 - 3x^2}}{2} \text{ and } y = \frac{-x - \sqrt{16 - 3x^2}}{2}$$

Use a graphing calculator to display the graphs of the following equations. State the type of curve each graph represents.

1. $y^2 + xy = 8$

2. $x^2 + y^2 - 2xy - x = 0$

3. $x^2 - xy + y^2 = 15$

4. $x^2 + xy + y^2 = -9$

5. $2x^2 - 2xy - y^2 + 4x = 20$

6. $x^2 - xy - 2y^2 + 2x + 5y - 3 = 0$

Enrichment

Graphing Quadratic Equations with xy-Terms

You can use a graphing calculator to examine graphs of
quadratic equations that contain xy-terms.

Example: Use a graphing calculator to display
the graph of $x^2 + xy + y^2 = 4$.

Solve the equation for y in terms of x
by using the quadratic formula.

$$y^2 + xy + (x^2 - 4) = 0$$

To use the formula, let $a = 1$, $b = x$,
and $c = (x^2 - 4)$.

$$y = \frac{-x \pm \sqrt{x^2 - 4(1)(x^2 - 4)}}{2}$$

$$y = \frac{-x \pm \sqrt{16 - 3x^2}}{2}$$

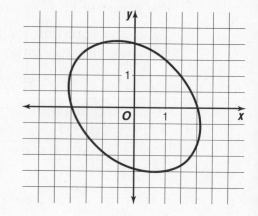

To graph the equation on the graphing
calculator, enter the two equations:

$$y = \frac{-x + \sqrt{16 - 3x^2}}{2} \text{ and } y = \frac{-x - \sqrt{16 - 3x^2}}{2}$$

**Use a graphing calculator to display the graphs of the
following equations. State the type of curve each graph
represents.**

1. $y^2 + xy = 8$ **hyperbola**

2. $x^2 + y^2 - 2xy - x = 0$ **parabola**

3. $x^2 - xy + y^2 = 15$ **ellipse**

4. $x^2 + xy + y^2 = -9$ **graph is ∅**

5. $2x^2 - 2xy - y^2 + 4x = 20$
hyperbola

6. $x^2 - xy - 2y^2 + 2x + 5y - 3 = 0$
two intersecting lines

Enrichment

Approximation by Means of Polynomials

Many scientific experiments produce pairs of numbers $[x, f(x)]$ that one would like to see related by some kind of formula. If the pairs form a function, you can fit a polynomial to the pairs in exactly one way. Consider the pairs given by the following table.

x	1	2	4	7
$f(x)$	6	11	39	−54

We will assume the polynomial is of degree three. Substitute the given values into this expression.

$$f(x) = A + B(x - x_0) + C(x - x_0)(x - x_1) + D(x - x_0)(x - x_1)(x - x_2)$$

You will get the system of equations shown at the right. You can solve this system and use the values for A, B, C, and D to find the desired polynomial.

$$6 = A$$
$$11 = A + B$$
$$39 = A + 3B + 6C$$
$$-54 = A + 6B + 30C + 90D$$

Solve each problem.

1. Solve the system of equations for the values A, B, C, and D.

2. Find the polynomial that represents the four ordered pairs. Write your answer in the form $y = a + bx + cx^2 + dx^3$.

3. Find the polynomial that gives the following values.

x	8	12	15	20
$f(x)$	−207	169	976	3801

4. A scientist measured the volume $f(x)$ of carbon dioxide gas that can be absorbed by one cubic centimeter of charcoal at pressure x.

x	120	340	534	698
$f(x)$	3.1	5.5	7.1	8.3

Find the values for A, B, C, and D.

NAME_____ DATE _____

Enrichment

Approximation by Means of Polynomials

Many scientific experiments produce pairs of numbers $[x, f(x)]$ that one would like to see related by some kind of formula. If the pairs form a function, you can fit a polynomial to the pairs in exactly one way. Consider the pairs given by the following table.

x	1	2	4	7
$f(x)$	6	11	39	−54

We will assume the polynomial is of degree three. Substitute the given values into this expression.

$$f(x) = A + B(x - x_0) + C(x - x_0)(x - x_1) + D(x - x_0)(x - x_1)(x - x_2)$$

You will get the system of equations shown at the right. You can solve this system and use the values for A, B, C, and D to find the desired polynomial.

$$6 = A$$
$$11 = A + B$$
$$39 = A + 3B + 6C$$
$$-54 = A + 6B + 30C + 90D$$

Solve each problem.

1. Solve the system of equations for the values A, B, C, and D.
   $A = 6$, $B = 5$, $C = 3$, $D = -2$

2. Find the polynomial that represents the four ordered pairs. Write your answer in the form $y = a + bx + cx^2 + dx^3$.
   $y = -2x^3 + 17x^2 - 32x + 23$

3. Find the polynomial that gives the following values.

x	8	12	15	20
$f(x)$	−207	169	976	3801

   $A = -207$, $B = 94$, $C = 25$, $D = 1$; $y = x^3 - 10x^2 - 10x + 1$

4. A scientist measured the volume $f(x)$ of carbon dioxide gas that can be absorbed by one cubic centimeter of charcoal at pressure x.

x	120	340	534	698
$f(x)$	3.1	5.5	7.1	8.3

   Find the values for A, B, C, and D.
   $A = 3.1$, $B = 0.01091$,
   $C = -0.00000643$, $D = 0.0000000066$

Enrichment

Student Edition
Pages 486–492

Miniature Golf

In miniature golf, the object of the game is to roll the golf ball into the hole in as few shots as possible. As in the diagram at the right, the hole is often placed so that a direct shot is impossible. Reflections can be used to help determine the direction that the ball should be rolled in order to score a hole-in-one.

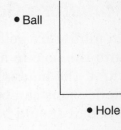

Example: Using wall $\overline{EF}$, find the path to use to score a hole-in-one.

Find the reflection image of the "hole" with respect to $\overline{EF}$ and label it H'. The intersection of $\overline{BH'}$ with wall $\overline{EF}$ is the point at which the shot should be directed.

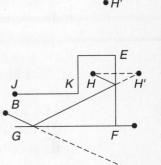

Example: For the hole at the right, find a path to score a hole-in-one.

Find the reflection image of H with respect to $\overline{EF}$ and label it H'. In this case, $\overline{BH'}$ intersects $\overline{JK}$ before intersecting $\overline{EF}$. Thus, this path cannot be used. To find a usable path, find the reflection image of H' with respect to $\overline{GF}$ and label it H''. Now, the intersection of $\overline{BH''}$ with wall $\overline{GF}$ is the point at which the shot should be directed.

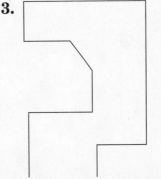

Copy each figure. Then, use reflections to determine a possible path for a hole-in-one.

1.

2.

3.

NAME_____ DATE _____

Enrichment

Miniature Golf

In miniature golf, the object of the game is to roll the golf ball into the hole in as few shots as possible. As in the diagram at the right, the hole is often placed so that a direct shot is impossible. Reflections can be used to help determine the direction that the ball should be rolled in order to score a hole-in-one.

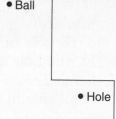

Example: Using wall $\overline{EF}$, find the path to use to score a hole-in-one.

Find the reflection image of the "hole" with respect to $\overline{EF}$ and label it H'. The intersection of $\overline{BH'}$ with wall $\overline{EF}$ is the point at which the shot should be directed.

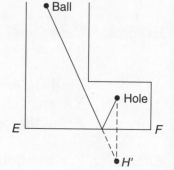

Example: For the hole at the right, find a path to score a hole-in-one.

Find the reflection image of H with respect to $\overline{EF}$ and label it H'. In this case, $\overline{BH'}$ intersects $\overline{JK}$ before intersecting $\overline{EF}$. Thus, this path cannot be used. To find a usable path, find the reflection image of H' with respect to $\overline{GF}$ and label it H''. Now, the intersection of $\overline{BH''}$ with wall $\overline{GF}$ is the point at which the shot should be directed.

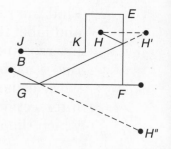

Copy each figure. Then, use reflections to determine a possible path for a hole-in-one.

1.
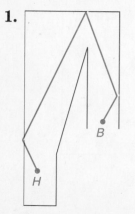

2.
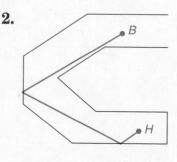

3.
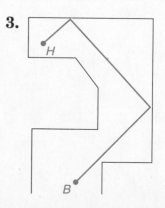

8-3

Enrichment

Odd and Even Polynomial Functions

Functions whose graphs are symmetric with respect to the origin are called *odd* functions. If $f(-x) = -f(x)$ for all x in the domain of $f(x)$, then $f(x)$ is odd.

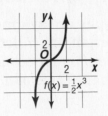

Functions whose graphs are symmetric with respect to the y-axis are called *even* functions. If $f(-x) = f(x)$ for all x in the domain of $f(x)$, then $f(x)$ is even.

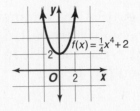

Example: Determine whether $f(x) = x^3 - 3x$ is odd, even, or neither.

$$f(x) = x^3 - 3x$$
$$f(-x) = (-x)^3 - 3(-x)$$
$$= -x^3 + 3x$$
$$= -(x^3 - 3x)$$
$$= -f(x)$$

Therefore, $f(x)$ is odd.

You can verify this conclusion by graphing the function. The graph of the function is symmetric with respect to the origin.

Determine whether each function is odd, even, or neither by graphing or by applying the rules for odd and even functions.

1. $f(x) = 4x^2$

2. $f(x) = -7x^4$

3. $f(x) = x^7$

4. $f(x) = x^3 - x^2$

5. $f(x) = 3x^3 + 1$

6. $f(x) = x^8 - x^5 - 6$

7. $f(x) = -8x^5 - 2x^3 + 6x$

8. $f(x) = x^4 - 3x^3 + 2x^2 - 6x + 1$

9. $f(x) = x^4 + 3x^2 + 11$

10. $f(x) = x^7 - 6x^5 + 2x^3 + x$

11. Complete the following definitions: A polynomial function is odd if and only if all the terms are of _____ degrees. A polynomial function is even if and only if all the terms are of _____ degrees.

Odd and Even Polynomial Functions

Functions whose graphs are symmetric with respect to the origin are called *odd* functions. If $f(-x) = -f(x)$ for all x in the domain of $f(x)$, then $f(x)$ is odd.

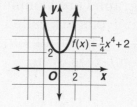

Functions whose graphs are symmetric with respect to the y-axis are called *even* functions. If $f(-x) = f(x)$ for all x in the domain of $f(x)$, then $f(x)$ is even.

Example: Determine whether $f(x) = x^3 - 3x$ is odd, even, or neither.

$$f(x) = x^3 - 3x$$
$$f(-x) = (-x)^3 - 3(-x)$$
$$= -x^3 + 3x$$
$$= -(x^3 - 3x)$$
$$= -f(x)$$

Therefore, $f(x)$ is odd.

You can verify this conclusion by graphing the function. The graph of the function is symmetric with respect to the origin.

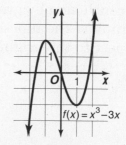

Determine whether each function is odd, even, or neither by graphing or by applying the rules for odd and even functions.

1. $f(x) = 4x^2$ **even**

2. $f(x) = -7x^4$ **even**

3. $f(x) = x^7$ **odd**

4. $f(x) = x^3 - x^2$ **neither**

5. $f(x) = 3x^3 + 1$ **neither**

6. $f(x) = x^8 - x^5 - 6$ **neither**

7. $f(x) = -8x^5 - 2x^3 + 6x$ **odd**

8. $f(x) = x^4 - 3x^3 + 2x^2 - 6x + 1$ **neither**

9. $f(x) = x^4 + 3x^2 + 11$ **even**

10. $f(x) = x^7 - 6x^5 + 2x^3 + x$ **odd**

11. Complete the following definitions: A polynomial function is odd if and only if all the terms are of ___**odd**___ degrees. A polynomial function is even if and only if all the terms are of ___**even**___ degrees.

Enrichment

Using Maximum Values

Many times maximum solutions are needed for different situations. For instance, what is the area of the largest rectangular field that can be enclosed with 2000 feet of fencing?

Let x and y denote the length and width of the field, respectively.

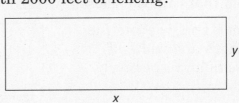

Perimeter: $2x + 2y = 2000 \rightarrow y = 1000 - x$
Area: $A = xy = x(1000 - x) = -x^2 + 1000x$

This problem is equivalent to finding the highest point on the graph of $A(x) = -x^2 + 1000x$ shown on the right.

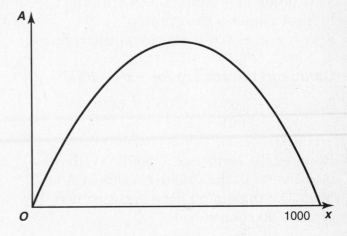

Complete the square for $-x^2 + 1000x$.

$A = -(x^2 - 1000x + 500^2) + 500^2$
$ = -(x - 500)^2 + 500^2$

Because the term $-(x - 500)^2$ is either negative or 0, the greatest value of A is 500^2. The maximum area enclosed is 500^2 or 250,000 square feet.

Solve each problem.

1. Find the area of the largest rectangular garden that can be enclosed by 300 feet of fence.

2. A farmer will make a rectangular pen with 100 feet of fence using part of his barn for one side of the pen. What is the largest area he can enclose?

3. An area along a straight stone wall is to be fenced. There are 600 meters of fencing available. What is the greatest rectangular area that can be enclosed?

Enrichment

Using Maximum Values

Many times maximum solutions are needed for different situations. For instance, what is the area of the largest rectangular field that can be enclosed with 2000 feet of fencing?

Let x and y denote the length and width of the field, respectively.

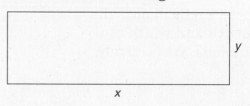

Perimeter: $2x + 2y = 2000 \rightarrow y = 1000 - x$
Area: $A = xy = x(1000 - x) = -x^2 + 1000x$

This problem is equivalent to finding the highest point on the graph of $A(x) = -x^2 + 1000x$ shown on the right.

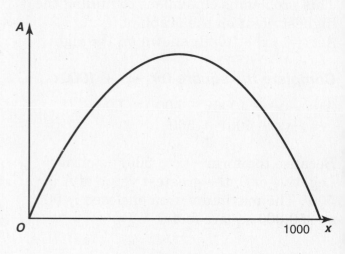

Complete the square for $-x^2 + 1000x$.

$A = -(x^2 - 1000x + 500^2) + 500^2$
$\ \ = -(x - 500)^2 + 500^2$

Because the term $-(x - 500)^2$ is either negative or 0, the greatest value of A is 500^2. The maximum area enclosed is 500^2 or 250,000 square feet.

Solve each problem.

1. Find the area of the largest rectangular garden that can be enclosed by 300 feet of fence. **5625 sq ft**

2. A farmer will make a rectangular pen with 100 feet of fence using part of his barn for one side of the pen. What is the largest area he can enclose? **1250 sq ft**

3. An area along a straight stone wall is to be fenced. There are 600 meters of fencing available. What is the greatest rectangular area that can be enclosed? **45,000 m²**

Enrichment

The Bisection Method for Approximating Real Zeros

The **bisection method** can be used to approximate zeros of polynomial functions like $f(x) = x^3 + x^2 - 3x - 3$. Since $f(1) = -4$ and $f(2) = 3$, there is at least one real zero between 1 and 2. The midpoint of this interval is $\frac{1+2}{2} = 1.5$. Since $f(1.5) = -1.875$, the zero is between 1.5 and 2. The midpoint of this interval is $\frac{1.5+2}{2} = 1.75$. Since $f(1.75)$ is about 0.172, the zero is between 1.5 and 1.75. The midpoint of this interval is $\frac{1.5+1.75}{2} = 1.625$ and $f(1.625)$ is about -0.94. The zero is between 1.625 and 1.75. The midpoint of this interval is $\frac{1.625+1.75}{2} = 1.6875$. Since $f(1.6875)$ is about -0.41, the zero is between 1.6875 and 1.75. Therefore, the zero is 1.7 to the nearest tenth. The diagram below summarizes the results obtained by the bisection method.

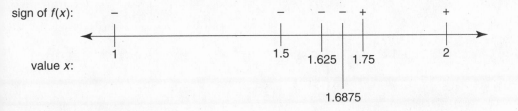

Using the bisection method, approximate to the nearest tenth the zero between the two integral values of x for each function.

1. $f(x) = x^3 - 4x^2 - 11x + 2$, $f(0) = 2$, $f(1) = -12$

2. $f(x) = 2x^4 + x^2 - 15$, $f(1) = -12$, $f(2) = 21$

3. $f(x) = x^5 - 2x^3 - 12$, $f(1) = -13$, $f(2) = 4$

4. $f(x) = 4x^3 - 2x + 7$, $f(-2) = -21$, $f(-1) = 5$

5. $f(x) = 3x^3 - 14x^2 - 27x + 126$, $f(4) = -14$, $f(5) = 16$

Enrichment

The Bisection Method for Approximating Real Zeros

The **bisection method** can be used to approximate zeros of polynomial functions like $f(x) = x^3 + x^2 - 3x - 3$. Since $f(1) = -4$ and $f(2) = 3$, there is at least one real zero between 1 and 2. The midpoint of this interval is $\frac{1 + 2}{2} = 1.5$. Since $f(1.5) = -1.875$, the zero is between 1.5 and 2. The midpoint of this interval is $\frac{1.5 + 2}{2} = 1.75$. Since $f(1.75)$ is about 0.172, the zero is between 1.5 and 1.75. The midpoint of this interval is $\frac{1.5 + 1.75}{2} = 1.625$ and $f(1.625)$ is about -0.94. The zero is between 1.625 and 1.75. The midpoint of this interval is $\frac{1.625 + 1.75}{2} = 1.6875$. Since $f(1.6875)$ is about -0.41, the zero is between 1.6875 and 1.75. Therefore, the zero is 1.7 to the nearest tenth. The diagram below summarizes the results obtained by the bisection method.

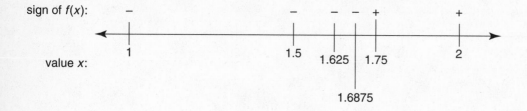

Using the bisection method, approximate to the nearest tenth the zero between the two integral values of x for each function.

1. $f(x) = x^3 - 4x^2 - 11x + 2$, $f(0) = 2$, $f(1) = -12$ **0.2**

2. $f(x) = 2x^4 + x^2 - 15$, $f(1) = -12$, $f(2) = 21$ **1.6**

3. $f(x) = x^5 - 2x^3 - 12$, $f(1) = -13$, $f(2) = 4$ **1.9**

4. $f(x) = 4x^3 - 2x + 7$, $f(-2) = -21$, $f(-1) = 5$ **−1.3**

5. $f(x) = 3x^3 - 14x^2 - 27x + 126$, $f(4) = -14$, $f(5) = 16$ **4.7**

Enrichment

Infinite Continued Fractions

Some infinite expressions are actually equal to real numbers! The infinite continued fraction at the right is one example.

$$x = 1 + \cfrac{1}{1 + \cfrac{1}{1 + \cfrac{1}{1 + \cfrac{1}{1 + \ldots}}}}$$

If you use x to stand for the infinite fraction, then the entire denominator of the first fraction on the right is also equal to x. This observation leads to the following equation:

$$x = 1 + \frac{1}{x}$$

Write a decimal for each continued fraction.

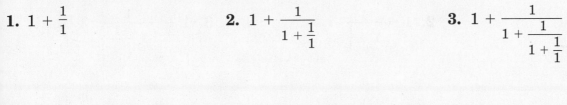

1. $1 + \cfrac{1}{1}$

2. $1 + \cfrac{1}{1 + \cfrac{1}{1}}$

3. $1 + \cfrac{1}{1 + \cfrac{1}{1 + \cfrac{1}{1}}}$

4. $1 + \cfrac{1}{1 + \cfrac{1}{1 + \cfrac{1}{1 + \cfrac{1}{1}}}}$

5. $1 + \cfrac{1}{1 + \cfrac{1}{1 + \cfrac{1}{1 + \cfrac{1}{1 + \cfrac{1}{1}}}}}$

6. The more terms you add to the fractions above, the closer their value approaches the value of the infinite continued fraction. What value do the fractions seem to be approaching?

7. Rewrite $x = 1 + \dfrac{1}{x}$ as a quadratic equation and solve for x.

8. Find the value of the following infinite continued fraction.

$$3 + \cfrac{1}{3 + \cfrac{1}{3 + \cfrac{1}{3 + \cfrac{1}{3 + \ldots}}}}$$

Infinite Continued Fractions

Some infinite expressions are actually equal to real numbers! The infinite continued fraction at the right is one example.

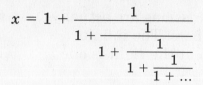

$$x = 1 + \cfrac{1}{1 + \cfrac{1}{1 + \cfrac{1}{1 + \cfrac{1}{1 + \ldots}}}}$$

If you use x to stand for the infinite fraction, then the entire denominator of the first fraction on the right is also equal to x. This observation leads to the following equation:

$$x = 1 + \frac{1}{x}$$

Write a decimal for each continued fraction.

1. $1 + \dfrac{1}{1}$ **2**

2. $1 + \cfrac{1}{1 + \frac{1}{1}}$ **1.5**

3. $1 + \cfrac{1}{1 + \cfrac{1}{1 + \frac{1}{1}}}$ **1.666̄**

4. $1 + \cfrac{1}{1 + \cfrac{1}{1 + \cfrac{1}{1 + \frac{1}{1}}}}$ **1.6**

5. $1 + \cfrac{1}{1 + \cfrac{1}{1 + \cfrac{1}{1 + \cfrac{1}{1 + \frac{1}{1}}}}}$ **1.625**

6. The more terms you add to the fractions above, the closer their value approaches the value of the infinite continued fraction. What value do the fractions seem to be approaching? **about 1.6**

7. Rewrite $x = 1 + \dfrac{1}{x}$ as a quadratic equation and solve for x.
$x^2 - x - 1 = 0; x = \dfrac{1 \pm}{} ; x \approx 1.618$ or -0.618

(The positive root is the value of the infinite fraction, because the original fraction is clearly not negative.)

8. Find the value of the following infinite continued fraction.

$$3 + \cfrac{1}{3 + \cfrac{1}{3 + \cfrac{1}{3 + \frac{1}{3 + \ldots}}}}$$ **$x = 3 + \dfrac{1}{x}; x = \dfrac{3 + \sqrt{13}}{2}$ or about 3.30**

NAME_____

DATE _____

Enrichment

Student Edition
Pages 525–528

Relative Maximum Values

The graph shows a relative maximum value somewhere between $f(-2)$ and $f(-1)$. You can obtain a closer approximation by comparing values such as those shown in the table.

$$f(x) = x^3 - 6x - 9$$

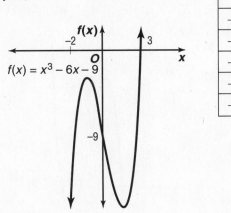

x	f(x)
-2	-5
-1.5	-3.375
-1.4	-3.344
-1.3	-3.397
-1	-4

To the nearest tenth a relative maximum value for $f(x)$ is -3.3.

Using a calculator to find points, graph each function. To the nearest tenth, find a relative maximum value of the function.

1. $f(x) = x(x^2 - 3)$

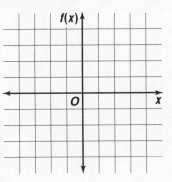

2. $f(x) = x^3 - 3x - 3$

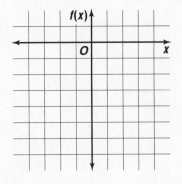

3. $f(x) = x^3 - 9x - 2$

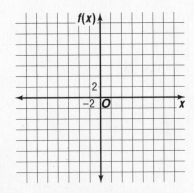

4. $f(x) = x^3 + 2x^2 - 12x - 24$

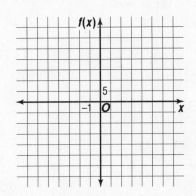

Enrichment

Relative Maximum Values

The graph shows a relative maximum value somewhere between $f(-2)$ and $f(-1)$. You can obtain a closer approximation by comparing values such as those shown in the table.

$f(x) = x^3 - 6x - 9$

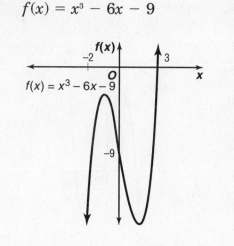

x	f(x)
-2	-5
-1.5	-3.375
-1.4	-3.344
-1.3	-3.397
-1	-4

To the nearest tenth a relative maximum value for $f(x)$ is -3.3.

Using a calculator to find points, graph each function. To the nearest tenth, find a relative maximum value of the function.

1. $f(x) = x(x^2 - 3)$
   relative max of 2.0

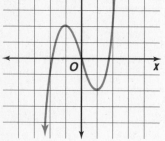

2. $f(x) = x^3 - 3x - 3$
   relative max of -1.0

3. $f(x) = x^3 - 9x - 2$
   relative max of 8.4

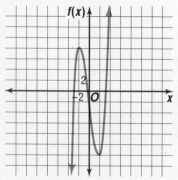

4. $f(x) = x^3 + 2x^2 - 12x - 24$
   relative max of 3.3

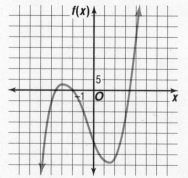

Enrichment

Proof by Induction

Mathematical induction is a useful tool when you want to prove that a statement is true for all natural numbers.

The three steps in using induction are:
1. Prove that the statement is true for $n = 1$.
2. Prove that if the statement is true for the natural number n, it must also be true for $n + 1$.
3. Conclude that the statement is true for all natural numbers.

Follow the steps to complete each proof.

Theorem A: The sum of the first n odd natural numbers is equal to n^2.

1. Show that the theorem is true for $n = 1$.

2. Suppose $1 + 3 + 5 + \cdots + (2n - 1) = n^2$. Show that
   $1 + 3 + 5 + \cdots + (2n - 1) + (2n + 1) = (n + 1)^2$.

3. Summarize the results of problems 1 and 2.

Theorem B: Show that $a^n - b^n$ is exactly divisible by $a - b$ for n equal to 1, 2, 3, and all natural numbers.

4. Show that the theorem is true for $n = 1$.

5. The expression $a^{n+1} - b^{n+1}$ can be rewritten as
   $a(a^n - b^n) + b^n(a - b)$. Verify that this is true.

6. Suppose $a - b$ is a factor of $a^n - b^n$. Use the result in problem 5 to show that $a - b$ must then also be a factor of $a^{n+1} - b^{n+1}$.

7. Summarize the results of problems 4 through 6.

Enrichment

Proof by Induction

Mathematical induction is a useful tool when you want to prove that a statement is true for all natural numbers.

The three steps in using induction are:
1. Prove that the statement is true for $n = 1$.
2. Prove that if the statement is true for the natural number n, it must also be true for $n + 1$.
3. Conclude that the statement is true for all natural numbers.

Follow the steps to complete each proof.

Theorem A: The sum of the first n odd natural numbers is equal to n^2.

1. Show that the theorem is true for $n = 1$.
   $1 = (1)^2$

2. Suppose $1 + 3 + 5 + \cdots + (2n - 1) = n^2$. Show that
   $1 + 3 + 5 + \cdots + (2n - 1) + (2n + 1) = (n + 1)^2$.
   Add $2n + 1$ to each side of the equation whose truth was assumed: $1 + 3 + 5 + \cdots + (2n - 1) + (2n + 1) = n^2 + (2n + 1) = (n + 1)^2$

3. Summarize the results of problems 1 and 2.
   The theorem is true for $n = 1$. *If the sum of the first n odd numbers equals n^2*, then it is true that the sum of the first $n + 1$ odd numbers equals $(n + 1)^2$. Therefore, the theorem is true for all natural numbers.

Theorem B: Show that $a^n - b^n$ is exactly divisible by $a - b$ for n equal to 1, 2, 3, and all natural numbers.

4. Show that the theorem is true for $n = 1$.
   $(a^1 - b^1) \div (a - b) = 1$

5. The expression $a^{n+1} - b^{n+1}$ can be rewritten as
   $a(a^n - b^n) + b^n(a - b)$. Verify that this is true.
   $a(a^n - b^n) + b^n(a - b) = a^{n+1} - ab^n + ab^n - b^{n+1} = a^{n+1} - b^{n+1}$

6. Suppose $a - b$ is a factor of $a^n - b^n$. Use the result in problem 5 to show that $a - b$ must then also be a factor of $a^{n+1} - b^{n+1}$.
   $a^{n+1} - b^{n+1} = a(a^n - b^n) + b^n(a - b)$; $a - b$ is a factor of both addends on the right side. So, $a - b$ is also a factor of the left side.

7. Summarize the results of problems 4 through 6.
   The theorem is true for $n = 1$. If $a - b$ is a factor of $a^n - b^n$, it is also a factor of $a^{n+1} - b^{n+1}$. So, the theorem is true for all natural numbers n.

NAME_____ DATE_____

Enrichment

Student Edition
Pages 550–555

Finding Maximum or Minimum Values

Many problems require finding a maximum or minimum value.
Such problems can often be solved by first writing a system of
equations, and then writing a function of one variable. By
graphing or making a table of values for the function, the
maximum or minimum value can be found. Diagrams are
often helpful for writing the initial system equations.

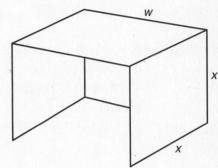

Example: A road salt storage shed is to be built with
two square sides, a back, and a top. The
shed is to be constructed of 900 square feet
of corrugated steel. Find the dimensions for
which the volume will be a maximum.

Let x represent the height and depth. Let w
represent the width. Since the surface area is to
be 900 square feet, $2x^2 + 2xw = 900$. Therefore,
$w = \dfrac{450 - x^2}{x}$. The volume is given by $V = x^2w$.
Substituting for w, $V = 450x - x^3$. By making a
graph on a table of values for $V(x)$, you can show that
there is a relative maximum which occurs when x is
about 12.2 feet. The value of w will be about 24.5 feet.

Solve each problem.

1. A store owner wants to construct a 1000-square-foot
rectangular display enclosure in the store's parking lot.
Three sides are to be chainlink fencing which costs $9.00 per
running foot. The fourth side is to be a brick wall which costs
$18.75 per running foot. Find the dimensions that will
minimize the cost.

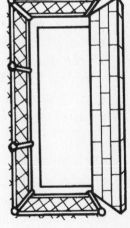

2. Gloria wants to make a rectangular patio along the back of
her house. She plans to surround the patio on three sides
with one foot square flagstones. She has 118 flagstones. Find
the maximum area of the patio not including the area of the
flagstones.

Algebra 2

Finding Maximum or Minimum Values

Many problems require finding a maximum or minimum value.
Such problems can often be solved by first writing a system of
equations, and then writing a function of one variable. By
graphing or making a table of values for the function, the
maximum or minimum value can be found. Diagrams are
often helpful for writing the initial system equations.

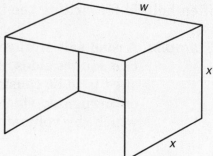

Example: A road salt storage shed is to be built with
two square sides, a back, and a top. The
shed is to be constructed of 900 square feet
of corrugated steel. Find the dimensions for
which the volume will be a maximum.

Let x represent the height and depth. Let w
represent the width. Since the surface area is to
be 900 square feet, $2x^2 + 2xw = 900$. Therefore,
$w = \dfrac{450 - x^2}{x}$. The volume is given by $V = x^2w$.
Substituting for w, $V = 450x - x^3$. By making a
graph on a table of values for $V(x)$, you can show that
there is a relative maximum which occurs when x is
about 12.2 feet. The value of w will be about 24.5 feet.

Solve each problem.

1. A store owner wants to construct a 1000-square-foot
rectangular display enclosure in the store's parking lot.
Three sides are to be chainlink fencing which costs $9.00 per
running foot. The fourth side is to be a brick wall which costs
$18.75 per running foot. Find the dimensions that will
minimize the cost.
length = 39.2 feet; width = 25.5 feet

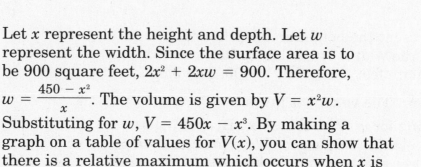

2. Gloria wants to make a rectangular patio along the back of
her house. She plans to surround the patio on three sides
with one foot square flagstones. She has 118 flagstones. Find
the maximum area of the patio not including the area of the
flagstones. 1740.5 square feet

Reading Algebra

In mathematics, the term *group* has a special meaning. The following numbered sentences discuss the idea of group and one interesting example of a group.

01 To be a group, a set of elements and a binary operation must satisfy four conditions: the set must be closed under the operation, the operation must be associative, there must be an identity element, and every element must have an inverse.

02 The following six functions form a group under the operation of composition of functions: $f_1(x) = x$, $f_2(x) = \dfrac{1}{x}$, $f_3(x) = 1 - x$, $f_4(x) = \dfrac{(x-1)}{x}$, $f_5(x) = \dfrac{x}{(x-1)}$, and $f_6(x) = \dfrac{1}{(1-x)}$.

03 This group is an example of a noncommutative group. For example, $f_3 \circ f_2 = f_4$, but $f_2 \circ f_3 = f_6$.

04 Some experimentation with this group will show that the identity element is f_1.

05 Every element is its own inverse except for f_4 and f_6, each of which is the inverse of the other.

Use the paragraph to answer these questions.

1. Explain what it means to say that a set is *closed* under an operation. Is the set of positive integers closed under subtraction?

2. Subtraction is a noncommutative operation for the set of integers. Write an informal definition of noncommutative.

3. For the set of integers, what is the identity element for the operation of multiplication? Justify your answer.

4. Explain how the following statement relates to sentence 05:

$$(f_6 \cdot f_4)(x) = f_6[f_4(x)] = f_6\!\left(\frac{x-1}{x}\right) = \frac{1}{1 - \frac{(x-1)}{x}} = x = f_1(x).$$

Enrichment

Reading Algebra

In mathematics, the term *group* has a special meaning. The following numbered sentences discuss the idea of group and one interesting example of a group.

01 To be a group, a set of elements and a binary operation must satisfy four conditions: the set must be closed under the operation, the operation must be associative, there must be an identity element, and every element must have an inverse.

02 The following six functions form a group under the operation of composition of functions: $f_1(x) = x$, $f_2(x) = \dfrac{1}{x}$, $f_3(x) = 1 - x$, $f_4(x) = \dfrac{(x - 1)}{x}$, $f_5(x) = \dfrac{x}{(x - 1)}$, and $f_6(x) = \dfrac{1}{(1 - x)}$.

03 This group is an example of a noncommutative group. For example, $f_3 \circ f_2 = f_4$, but $f_2 \circ f_3 = f_6$.

04 Some experimentation with this group will show that the identity element is f_1.

05 Every element is its own inverse except for f_4 and f_6, each of which is the inverse of the other.

Use the paragraph to answer these questions.

1. Explain what it means to say that a set is *closed* under an operation. Is the set of positive integers closed under subtraction? **Performing the operation on any two elements of the set results in an element of the same set. No, 3 and 4 are positive integers but 3 − 4 is not.**

2. Subtraction is a noncommutative operation for the set of integers. Write an informal definition of noncommutative. **The order in which the elements are used with the operation can affect the result.**

3. For the set of integers, what is the identity element for the operation of multiplication? Justify your answer. **1, because, for every integer a, $a \cdot 1 = a$ and $1 \cdot a = a$.**

4. Explain how the following statement relates to sentence 05:

$$(f_6 \cdot f_4)(x) = f_6[f_4(x)] = f_6\left(\dfrac{x - 1}{x}\right) = \dfrac{1}{\dfrac{1 - (x - 1)}{x}} = x = f_1(x).$$

It shows that f_4 is the inverse of f_6.

Enrichment

Expansions of Rational Expressions

Many rational expressions can be transformed into a **power series.** A power series is an infinite series of the form $A + Bx + Cx^2 + Dx^3 + \cdots$. The rational expression and the power series normally can be said to have the same values only for certain values of x. For example, the following equation holds only for values of x such that $-1 < x < 1$.

$$\frac{1}{1-x} = 1 + x + x^2 + x^3 + \cdots \text{ for } -1 < x < 1$$

Example: Expand $\dfrac{2 + 3x}{1 + x + x^2}$ in ascending powers of x.

Assume that the expression equals a series of the form $A + Bx + Cx^2 + Dx^3 + \cdots$. Then multiply both sides of the equation by the denominator $1 + x + x^2$.

$$\frac{2 + 3x}{1 + x + x^2} = A + Bx + Cx^2 + Dx^3 + \cdots$$

$$2 + 3x = (1 + x + x^2)(A + Bx + Cx^2 + Dx^3 + \cdots)$$

$$2 + 3x = A + Bx + Cx^2 + Dx^3 + \cdots$$
$$\qquad + Ax + Bx^2 + Cx^3 + \cdots$$
$$\qquad\qquad + Ax^2 + Bx^3 + \cdots$$

$$2 + 3x = A + (B + A)x + (C + B + A)x^2 + (D + C + B)x^3 + \cdots$$

Now, match the coefficients of the polynomials.

$2 = A$

$3 = B + A$

$0 = C + B + A$

$0 = D + C + B + A$

Finally, solve for A, B, C, and D and write the expansion.

$A = 2$, $B = 1$, $C = -3$, and $D = 0$

Therefore, $\dfrac{2 + 3x}{1 + x + x^2} = 2 + x - 3x^2 + \cdots$

Expand each rational expression to four terms.

1. $\dfrac{1 - x}{1 + x + x^2}$

2. $\dfrac{2}{1 - x}$

3. $\dfrac{1}{1 + x}$

Enrichment

Expansions of Rational Expressions

Many rational expressions can be transformed into a **power series.** A power series is an infinite series of the form $A + Bx + Cx^2 + Dx^3 + \cdots$. The rational expression and the power series normally can be said to have the same values only for certain values of x. For example, the following equation holds only for values of x such that $-1 < x < 1$.

$$\frac{1}{1-x} = 1 + x + x^2 + x^3 + \cdots \text{ for } -1 < x < 1$$

Example: Expand $\dfrac{2 + 3x}{1 + x + x^2}$ in ascending powers of x.

Assume that the expression equals a series of the form $A + Bx + Cx^2 + Dx^3 + \cdots$. Then multiply both sides of the equation by the denominator $1 + x + x^2$.

$$\frac{2 + 3x}{1 + x + x^2} = A + Bx + Cx^2 + Dx^3 + \cdots$$

$$2 + 3x = (1 + x + x^2)(A + Bx + Cx^2 + Dx^3 + \cdots)$$

$$2 + 3x = A + Bx + Cx^2 + Dx^3 + \cdots$$
$$+ Ax + Bx^2 + Cx^3 + \cdots$$
$$+ Ax^2 + Bx^3 + \cdots$$

$$2 + 3x = A + (B + A)x + (C + B + A)x^2 + (D + C + B)x^3 + \cdots$$

Now, match the coefficients of the polynomials.

$2 = A$

$3 = B + A$

$0 = C + B + A$

$0 = D + C + B + A$

Finally, solve for A, B, C, and D and write the expansion.

$A = 2$, $B = 1$, $C = -3$, and $D = 0$

Therefore, $\dfrac{2 + 3x}{1 + x + x^2} = 2 + x - 3x^2 + \cdots$

Expand each rational expression to four terms.

1. $\dfrac{1 - x}{1 + x + x^2}$

$1 - 2x + x^2 + x^3 + \cdots$

2. $\dfrac{2}{1 - x}$

$2 + x + x^2 + x^3 + \cdots$

3. $\dfrac{1}{1 + x}$

$1 - x + x^2 - x^3 + \cdots$

Partial Fractions

It is sometimes an advantage to rewrite a rational expression as the sum of two or more fractions. For example, you might do this in a calculus course while carrying out a procedure called integration.

You can resolve a rational expression into partial fractions if two conditions are met:

(1) The degree of the numerator must be less than the degree of the denominator; and

(2) The factors of the denominator must be known.

Example: Resolve $\dfrac{3}{x^3 + 1}$ into partial fractions.

The denominator has two factors, a linear factor, $x + 1$, and a quadratic factor, $x^2 - x + 1$. Start by writing the following equation. Notice that the degree of the numerators of each partial fraction is less than its denominator.

$$\frac{3}{x^3 + 1} = \frac{A}{x + 1} + \frac{Bx + C}{x^2 - x + 1}$$

Now, multiply both sides of the equation by $x^3 + 1$ to clear the fractions and finish the problem by solving for the coefficients A, B, and C.

$$\frac{3}{x^3 + 1} = \frac{A}{x + 1} + \frac{Bx + C}{x^2 - x + 1}$$
$$3 = A(x^2 - x + 1) + (x + 1)(Bx + C)$$
$$3 = Ax^2 - Ax + A + Bx^2 + Cx + Bx + C$$
$$3 = (A + B)x^2 + (B + C - A)x + (A + C)$$

Equating each term,
$$0x^2 = (A + B)x^2$$
$$0x = (B + C - A)x$$
$$3 = (A + C)$$

Therefore, $A = 1$, $B = -1$, $C = 2$, and
$$\frac{3}{x^3 + 1} = \frac{1}{x + 1} + \frac{-x + 2}{x^2 - x + 1}.$$

Resolve each rational expression into partial fractions.

1. $\dfrac{5x - 3}{x^2 - 2x - 3} = \dfrac{A}{x + 1} + \dfrac{B}{x - 3}$

2. $\dfrac{6x + 7}{(x + 2)^2} = \dfrac{A}{x + 2} + \dfrac{B}{(x + 2)^2}$

3. $\dfrac{4x^3 - x^2 - 3x - 2}{x^2(x + 1)^2} = \dfrac{A}{x} + \dfrac{B}{x^2} + \dfrac{C}{x + 1} + \dfrac{D}{(x + 1)^2}$

Partial Fractions

It is sometimes an advantage to rewrite a rational expression as the sum of two or more fractions. For example, you might do this in a calculus course while carrying out a procedure called integration.

You can resolve a rational expression into partial fractions if two conditions are met:

(1) The degree of the numerator must be less than the degree of the denominator; and

(2) The factors of the denominator must be known.

Example: Resolve $\dfrac{3}{x^3 + 1}$ into partial fractions.

The denominator has two factors, a linear factor, $x + 1$, and a quadratic factor, $x^2 - x + 1$. Start by writing the following equation. Notice that the degree of the numerators of each partial fraction is less than its denominator.

$$\frac{3}{x^3 + 1} = \frac{A}{x + 1} + \frac{Bx + C}{x^2 - x + 1}$$

Now, multiply both sides of the equation by $x^3 + 1$ to clear the fractions and finish the problem by solving for the coefficients A, B, and C.

$$\frac{3}{x^3 + 1} = \frac{A}{x + 1} + \frac{Bx + C}{x^2 - x + 1}$$
$$3 = A(x^2 - x + 1) + (x + 1)(Bx + C)$$
$$3 = Ax^2 - Ax + A + Bx^2 + Cx + Bx + C$$
$$3 = (A + B)x^2 + (B + C - A)x + (A + C)$$

Equating each term,
$$0x^2 = (A + B)x^2$$
$$0x = (B + C - A)x$$
$$3 = (A + C)$$

Therefore, $A = 1$, $B = -1$, $C = 2$, and
$$\frac{3}{x^3 + 1} = \frac{1}{x + 1} + \frac{-x + 2}{x^2 - x + 1}.$$

Resolve each rational expression into partial fractions.

1. $\dfrac{5x - 3}{x^2 - 2x - 3} = \dfrac{A}{x + 1} + \dfrac{B}{x - 3}$ **A = 2, B = 3**

2. $\dfrac{6x + 7}{(x + 2)^2} = \dfrac{A}{x + 2} + \dfrac{B}{(x + 2)^2}$ **A = 6, B = −5**

3. $\dfrac{4x^3 - x^2 - 3x - 2}{x^2(x + 1)^2} = \dfrac{A}{x} + \dfrac{B}{x^2} + \dfrac{C}{x + 1} + \dfrac{D}{(x + 1)^2}$
A = 1, B = −2, C = 3, D = −4

Enrichment

Limits

Sequences of numbers with a rational expression for the
general term often approach some number as a finite limit.
For example, the reciprocals of the positive integers approach 0
as n gets larger and larger. This is written using the notation
shown below. The symbol ∞ stands for infinity and $n \to \infty$ means
that n is getting larger and larger, or "n goes to infinity."

$$1, \frac{1}{2}, \frac{1}{3}, \frac{1}{4}, \cdots, \frac{1}{n}, \cdots \qquad \lim_{n \to \infty} \frac{1}{n} = 0$$

Example: Find $\lim\limits_{n \to \infty} \dfrac{n^2}{(n + 1)^2}$

It is not immediately apparent whether the sequence
approaches a limit or not. But notice what happens if
we divide the numerator and denominator of the
general term by n^2.

$$\frac{n^2}{(n + 1)^2} = \frac{n^2}{n^2 + 2n + 1}$$

$$= \frac{\dfrac{n^2}{n^2}}{\dfrac{n^2}{n^2} + \dfrac{2n}{n^2} + \dfrac{1}{n^2}}$$

$$= \frac{1}{1 + \dfrac{2}{n} + \dfrac{1}{n^2}}$$

The two fractions in the denominator will approach a
limit of 0 as n gets very large, so the entire expression
approaches a limit of 1.

Find the following limits.

1. $\lim\limits_{n \to \infty} \dfrac{n^3 + 5n}{n^4 - 6}$

2. $\lim\limits_{n \to \infty} \dfrac{1 - n}{n^2}$

3. $\lim\limits_{n \to \infty} \dfrac{2(n + 1) + 1}{2n + 1}$

4. $\lim\limits_{n \to \infty} \dfrac{2n + 1}{1 - 3n}$

Enrichment

Limits

Sequences of numbers with a rational expression for the
general term often approach some number as a finite limit.
For example, the reciprocals of the positive integers approach 0
as n gets larger and larger. This is written using the notation
shown below. The symbol ∞ stands for infinity and $n \to \infty$ means
that n is getting larger and larger, or "n goes to infinity."

$$1, \frac{1}{2}, \frac{1}{3}, \frac{1}{4}, \cdots, \frac{1}{n}, \cdots \qquad \lim_{n \to \infty} \frac{1}{n} = 0$$

Example: Find $\lim\limits_{n \to \infty} \dfrac{n^2}{(n + 1)^2}$

It is not immediately apparent whether the sequence
approaches a limit or not. But notice what happens if
we divide the numerator and denominator of the
general term by n^2.

$$\frac{n^2}{(n + 1)^2} = \frac{n^2}{n^2 + 2n + 1}$$

$$= \frac{\dfrac{n^2}{n^2}}{\dfrac{n^2}{n^2} + \dfrac{2n}{n^2} + \dfrac{1}{n^2}}$$

$$= \frac{1}{1 + \dfrac{2}{n} + \dfrac{1}{n^2}}$$

The two fractions in the denominator will approach a
limit of 0 as n gets very large, so the entire expression
approaches a limit of 1.

Find the following limits.

1. $\lim\limits_{n \to \infty} \dfrac{n^3 + 5n}{n^4 - 6}$ **0**

2. $\lim\limits_{n \to \infty} \dfrac{1 - n}{n^2}$ **0**

3. $\lim\limits_{n \to \infty} \dfrac{2(n + 1) + 1}{2n + 1}$ **1**

4. $\lim\limits_{n \to \infty} \dfrac{2n + 1}{1 - 3n}$ $-\dfrac{2}{3}$

Finding Solutions of $x^y = y^x$

Perhaps you have noticed that if x and y are interchanged in equations such as $x = y$ and $xy = 1$, the resulting equation is equivalent to the original equation. The same is true of the equation $x^y = y^x$. However, finding solutions of $x^y = y^x$ and drawing its graph is not a simple process.

Solve each problem. Assume that x and y are positive real numbers.

1. If $a > 0$, will (a, a) be a solution of $x^y = y^x$? Justify your answer.

2. If $c > 0$, $d > 0$, and (c, d) is a solution of $x^y = y^x$, will (d, c) also be a solution? Justify your answer.

3. Use 2 as a value for y in $x^y = y^x$. The equation becomes $x^2 = 2^x$.

   a. Find equations for two functions, $f(x)$ and $g(x)$ that you could graph to find the solutions of $x^2 = 2^x$. Then graph the functions on a separate sheet of graph paper.

   b. Use the graph you drew for Part a to state two solutions for $x^2 = 2^x$. Then use these solutions to state two solutions for $x^y = y^x$.

4. In this exercise, a graphing calculator will be very helpful. Use the technique of Exercise 3 to complete the tables below. Then graph $x^y = y^x$ for positive values of x and y. If there are asymptotes, show them in your diagram using dotted lines. Note that in the table, some values of y call for one value of x, others call for two.

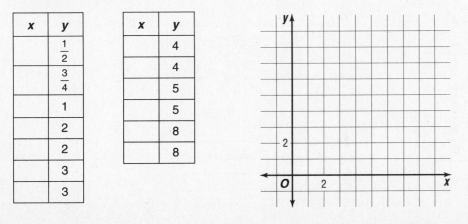

x	y
	$\frac{1}{2}$
	$\frac{3}{4}$
	1
	2
	2
	3
	3

x	y
	4
	4
	5
	5
	8
	8

Finding Solutions of $x^y = y^x$

Perhaps you have noticed that if x and y are interchanged in equations such as $x = y$ and $xy = 1$, the resulting equation is equivalent to the original equation. The same is true of the equation $x^y = y^x$. However, finding solutions of $x^y = y^x$ and drawing its graph is not a simple process.

Solve each problem. Assume that x and y are positive real numbers.

1. If $a > 0$, will (a, a) be a solution of $x^y = y^x$? Justify your answer.
   yes, since $a^a = a^a$ must be true (reflexive prop. of equality)

2. If $c > 0$, $d > 0$, and (c, d) is a solution of $x^y = y^x$, will (d, c) also be a solution? Justify your answer. **yes; Replacing x with d, y with c gives $d^c = c^d$; but if (c, d) is a solution, $c^d = d^c$. So, by the symmetric property of equality, $d^c = c^d$ is true.**

3. Use 2 as a value for y in $x^y = y^x$. The equation becomes $x^2 = 2^x$.

   a. Find equations for two functions, $f(x)$ and $g(x)$ that you could graph to find the solutions of $x^2 = 2^x$. Then graph the functions on a separate sheet of graph paper. $f(x) = x^2$, $g(x) = 2^x$
   See students' graphs.

   b. Use the graph you drew for Part a to state two solutions for $x^2 = 2^x$. Then use these solutions to state two solutions for $x^y = y^x$. **2, 4; (2, 2), (4, 2)**

4. In this exercise, a graphing calculator will be very helpful. Use the technique of Exercise 3 to complete the tables below. Then graph $x^y = y^x$ for positive values of x and y. If there are asymptotes, show them in your diagram using dotted lines. Note that in the table, some values of y call for one value of x, others call for two.

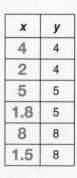

x	y
$\frac{1}{2}$	$\frac{1}{2}$
$\frac{3}{4}$	$\frac{3}{4}$
1	1
2	2
4	2
3	3
2.5	3

x	y
4	4
2	4
5	5
1.8	5
8	8
1.5	8

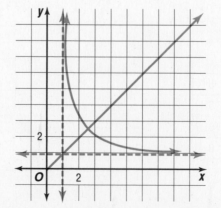

Enrichment

Musical Relationships

The frequencies of notes in a musical scale that are one octave apart are related by an exponential equation. For the eight C notes on a piano, the equation is $C_n = C_1 2^{n-1}$, where C_n represents the frequency of note C_n.

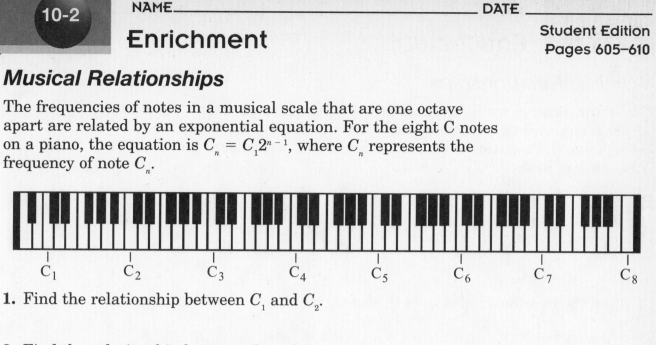

$C_1 \qquad C_2 \qquad C_3 \qquad C_4 \qquad C_5 \qquad C_6 \qquad C_7 \qquad C_8$

1. Find the relationship between C_1 and C_2.

2. Find the relationship between C_1 and C_4.

The frequencies of consecutive notes are related by a common ratio r. The general equation is $f_n = f_1 r^{n-1}$.

3. If the frequency of middle C is 261.6 cycles per second and the frequency of the next higher C is 523.2 cycles per second, find the common ratio r. (*Hint:* The two C's are 12 notes apart.) Write the answer as a radical expression.

C♯ D♯   F♯ G♯ A♯

C₁ D E F G A B C₂

4. Substitute decimal values for r and f_1 to find a specific equation for f_n.

5. Find the frequency of F♯ above middle C.

6. The frets on a guitar are spaced so that the sound made by pressing a string against one fret has about 1.0595 times the wavelength of the sound made by using the next fret. The general equation is $w_n = w_0(1.0595)^n$. Describe the arrangement of the frets on a guitar.

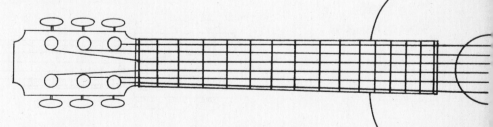

Enrichment

Musical Relationships

The frequencies of notes in a musical scale that are one octave apart are related by an exponential equation. For the eight C notes on a piano, the equation is $C_n = C_1 2^{n-1}$, where C_n represents the frequency of note C_n.

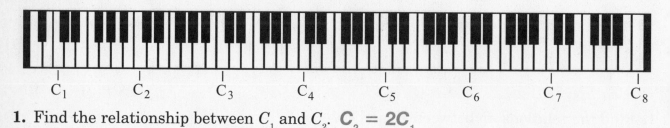

C_1 C_2 C_3 C_4 C_5 C_6 C_7 C_8

1. Find the relationship between C_1 and C_2. **$C_2 = 2C_1$**

2. Find the relationship between C_1 and C_4. **$C_4 = 8C_1$**

The frequencies of consecutive notes are related by a common ratio r. The general equation is $f_n = f_1 r^{n-1}$.

3. If the frequency of middle C is 261.6 cycles per second and the frequency of the next higher C is 523.2 cycles per second, find the common ratio r. (*Hint:* The two C's are 12 notes apart.) Write the answer as a radical expression.

$$r = \sqrt[12]{2}$$

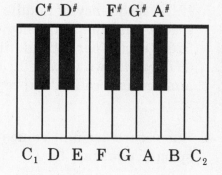

$C^\#$ $D^\#$ $F^\#$ $G^\#$ $A^\#$

C_1 D E F G A B C_2

4. Substitute decimal values for r and f_1 to find a specific equation for f_n.

$f_n = 261.1(1.05946)^{n-1}$

5. Find the frequency of $F^\#$ above middle C.

$f_7 = 261.6(1.05946)^6 \approx 369.95$

6. The frets on a guitar are spaced so that the sound made by pressing a string against one fret has about 1.0595 times the wavelength of the sound made by using the next fret. The general equation is $w_n = w_0(1.0595)^n$. Describe the arrangement of the frets on a guitar.
The frets are spaced in a logarithmic scale.

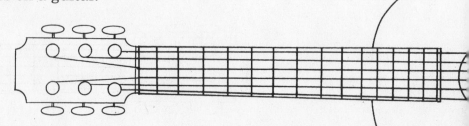

10-3

Enrichment

Spirals

Consider an angle in standard position with its vertex at a point O called the pole. Its initial side is on a coordinatized axis called the *polar axis*. A point P on the terminal side of the angle is named by the *polar coordinates* (r, θ), where r is the directed distance of the point from O and θ is the measure of the angle. Graphs in this system may be drawn on polar coordinate paper such as the kind shown below.

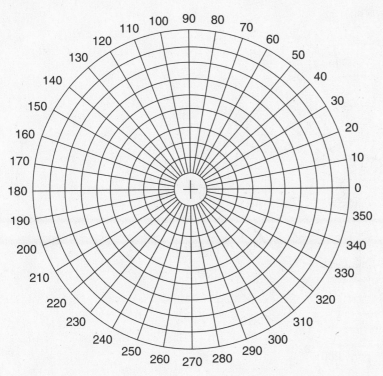

1. Use a calculator to complete the table for $\log_2 r = \dfrac{\theta}{120}$. (*Hint:* To find θ on a calculator, press 120 ⨉ r LOG ÷ 2 LOG.)

r	1	2	3	4	5	6	7	8

2. Plot the points found in Exercise 1 on the grid above and connect to form a smooth curve.

This type of spiral is called a logarithmic spiral because the angle measures are proportional to the logarithms of the radii.

NAME_____ DATE _____

Enrichment

Spirals

Consider an angle in standard position with its vertex at a point O called the pole. Its initial side is on a coordinatized axis called the *polar axis*. A point P on the terminal side of the angle is named by the *polar coordinates* (r, θ), where r is the directed distance of the point from O and θ is the measure of the angle. Graphs in this system may be drawn on polar coordinate paper such as the kind shown below.

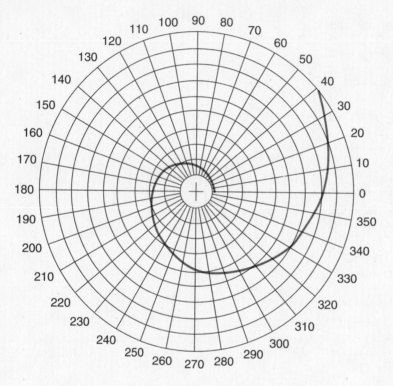

1. Use a calculator to complete the table for $\log_2 r = \dfrac{\theta}{120}$. (*Hint:* To find θ on a calculator, press 120 ⊠ r LOG ÷ 2 LOG.)

r	1	2	3	4	5	6	7	8
θ	0°	120°	190°	240°	279°	310°	337°	360°

2. Plot the points found in Exercise 1 on the grid above and connect to form a smooth curve.

   This type of spiral is called a logarithmic spiral because the angle measures are proportional to the logarithms of the radii.

Enrichment

Student Edition
Pages 617–621

The Slide Rule

Before the invention of electronic calculators, computations were often performed on a slide rule. A slide rule is based on the idea of logarithms. It has two movable rods labeled with C and D scales. Each of the scales is logarithmic.

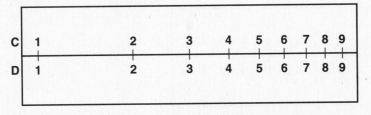

To multiply 2×3 on a slide rule, move the C rod to the right as shown below. You can find 2×3 by adding log 2 to log 3, and the slide rule adds the lengths for you. The distance you get is 0.778, or the logarithm of 6.

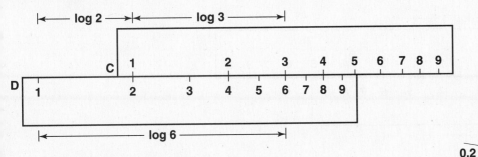

Follow the steps to make a slide rule.

1. Use graph paper that has small squares, such as 10 squares to the inch. Using the scales shown at the right, plot the curve $y = \log x$ for $x = 1, 1.5$, and the whole numbers from 2 through 10. Make an obvious heavy dot for each point plotted.

2. You will need two strips of cardboard. A 5-by-7 index card, cut in half the long way, will work fine. Turn the graph you made in Exercise 1 sideways and use it to mark a logarithmic scale on each of the two strips. The figure shows the mark for 2 being drawn.

3. Explain how to use a slide rule to divide 8 by 2.

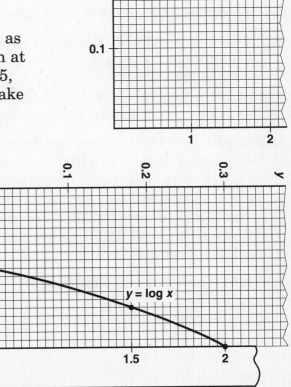

Enrichment

The Slide Rule

Before the invention of electronic calculators, computations were often performed on a slide rule. A slide rule is based on the idea of logarithms. It has two movable rods labeled with C and D scales. Each of the scales is logarithmic.

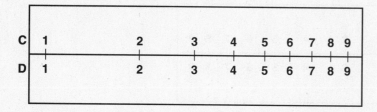

To multiply 2 × 3 on a slide rule, move the C rod to the right as shown below. You can find 2 × 3 by adding log 2 to log 3, and the slide rule adds the lengths for you. The distance you get is 0.778, or the logarithm of 6.

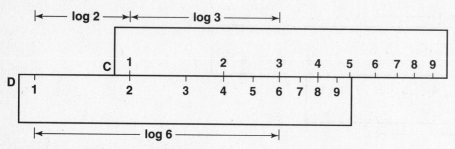

1-2 See students' work.

Follow the steps to make a slide rule.

1. Use graph paper that has small squares, such as 10 squares to the inch. Using the scales shown at the right, plot the curve $y = \log x$ for $x = 1, 1.5$, and the whole numbers from 2 through 10. Make an obvious heavy dot for each point plotted.

2. You will need two strips of cardboard. A 5-by-7 index card, cut in half the long way, will work fine. Turn the graph you made in Exercise 1 sideways and use it to mark a logarithmic scale on each of the two strips. The figure shows the mark for 2 being drawn.

3. Explain how to use a slide rule to divide 8 by 2. **Line up the 2 on the C scale with the 8 on the D scale. The quotient is the number on the D scale below the 1 on the C scale.**

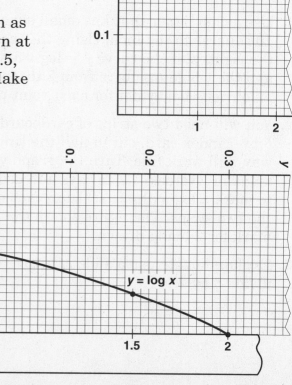

Algebra 2

Enrichment

Approximations for π and e

The following expression can be used to approximate e. If greater and greater values of n are used, the value of the expression approximates e more and more closely.

$$\left(1 + \frac{1}{n}\right)^n$$

Another way to approximate e is to use this infinite sum. The greater the value of n, the closer the approximation.

$$e = 1 + 1 + \frac{1}{2} + \frac{1}{2 \cdot 3} + \frac{1}{2 \cdot 3 \cdot 4} + \cdots + \frac{1}{2 \cdot 3 \cdot 4 \cdot \cdots \cdot n} + \cdots$$

In a similar manner, π can be approximated using an infinite product discovered by the English mathematician John Wallis (1616–1703).

$$\frac{\pi}{2} = \frac{2}{1} \cdot \frac{2}{3} \cdot \frac{4}{3} \cdot \frac{4}{5} \cdot \frac{6}{5} \cdot \frac{6}{7} \cdot \cdots \cdot \frac{2n}{2n-1} \cdot \frac{2n}{2n+1} \cdots$$

Solve each problem.

1. Use a calculator with an e^x key to find e to 7 decimal places.

2. Use the expression $\left(1 + \frac{1}{n}\right)^n$ to approximate e to 3 decimal places. Use 5, 100, 500, and 7000 as values of n.

3. Use the infinite sum to approximate e to 3 decimal places. Use the whole numbers from 3 through 6 as values of n.

4. Which approximation method approaches the value of e more quickly?

5. Use a calculator with a π key to find π to 7 decimal places.

6. Use the infinite product to approximate π to 3 decimal places. Use the whole numbers from 3 through 6 as values of n.

7. Does the infinite product give good approximations for π quickly?

8. Show that $\pi^4 + \pi^5$ is equal to e^6 to 4 decimal places.

9. Which is larger, e^π or π^e?

10. The expression $x^{\frac{1}{x}}$ reaches a maximum value at $x = e$. Use this fact to prove the inequality you found in Exercise 9.

Enrichment

Approximations for π and e

The following expression can be used to approximate e. If greater and greater values of n are used, the value of the expression approximates e more and more closely.

$$\left(1 + \frac{1}{n}\right)^n$$

Another way to approximate e is to use this infinite sum. The greater the value of n, the closer the approximation.

$$e = 1 + 1 + \frac{1}{2} + \frac{1}{2 \cdot 3} + \frac{1}{2 \cdot 3 \cdot 4} + \cdots + \frac{1}{2 \cdot 3 \cdot 4 \cdots \cdot n} + \cdots$$

In a similar manner, π can be approximated using an infinite product discovered by the English mathematician John Wallis (1616–1703).

$$\frac{\pi}{2} = \frac{2}{1} \cdot \frac{2}{3} \cdot \frac{4}{3} \cdot \frac{4}{5} \cdot \frac{6}{5} \cdot \frac{6}{7} \cdot \cdots \cdot \frac{2n}{2n - 1} \cdot \frac{2n}{2n + 1} \cdots$$

Solve each problem.

1. Use a calculator with an e^x key to find e to 7 decimal places. **2.7182818**

2. Use the expression $\left(1 + \frac{1}{n}\right)^n$ to approximate e to 3 decimal places. Use 5, 100, 500, and 7000 as values of n. **2.488, 2.705, 2.716, 2.718**

3. Use the infinite sum to approximate e to 3 decimal places. Use the whole numbers from 3 through 6 as values of n. **2.667, 2.708, 2.717, 2.718**

4. Which approximation method approaches the value of e more quickly? **the infinite sum**

5. Use a calculator with a π key to find π to 7 decimal places. **3.1415927**

6. Use the infinite product to approximate π to 3 decimal places. Use the whole numbers from 3 through 6 as values of n.
2.926, 2.972, 3.002, 3.023

7. Does the infinite product give good approximations for π quickly? **no**

8. Show that $\pi^4 + \pi^5$ is equal to e^6 to 4 decimal places.
To 4 decimal places, they both equal 403.4288.

9. Which is larger, e^π or π^e?
$e^\pi > \pi^e$

10. The expression $x^{\frac{1}{x}}$ reaches a maximum value at $x = e$. Use this fact to prove the inequality you found in Exercise 9.
$e^{\frac{1}{e}} > \pi^{\frac{1}{\pi}}$; $\left(e^{\frac{1}{e}}\right)^{\pi e} > \left(\pi^{\frac{1}{\pi}}\right)^{\pi e}$; $e^\pi > \pi^e$

Enrichment

Effective Annual Yield

When interest is compounded more than once per year, the effective annual yield is higher than the annual interest rate. The effective annual yield, E, is the interest rate that would give the same amount of interest if the interest were compounded once per year. If P dollars are invested for one year, the value of the investment at the end of the year is $A = P(1 + E)$. If P dollars are invested for one year at a nominal rate r compounded n times per year, the value of the investment at the end of the year is $A = P\left(1 + \frac{r}{n}\right)^n$. Setting the amounts equal and solving for E will produce a formula for the effective annual yield.

$$P(1 + E) = P\left(1 + \frac{r}{n}\right)^n$$
$$1 + E = \left(1 + \frac{r}{n}\right)^n$$
$$E = \left(1 + \frac{r}{n}\right)^n - 1$$

If compounding is continuous, the value of the investment at the end of one year is $A = Pe^r$. Again set the amounts equal and solve for E. A formula for the effective annual yield under continuous compounding is obtained.

$$P(1 + E) = Pe^r$$
$$1 + E = e^r$$
$$E = e^r - 1$$

Examples:

Find the effective annual yield of an investment made at 7.5% compounded monthly.

$r = 0.075$
$n = 12$
$E = \left(1 + \frac{0.075}{12}\right)^{12} - 1 \approx 7.76\%$

Find the effective annual yield of an investment made at 6.25% compounded continuously.

$r = 0.0625$
$E = e^{0.0625} - 1 \approx 6.45\%$

Find the effective annual yield for each investment.

1. 10% compounded quarterly

2. 8.5% compounded monthly

3. 9.25% compounded continuously

4. 7.75% compounded continuously

5. 6.5% compounded daily (assume a 365-day year)

6. Which investment yields more interest—9% compounded continuously or 9.2% compounded quarterly?

Algebra 2

Effective Annual Yield

When interest is compounded more than once per year, the effective annual yield is higher than the annual interest rate. The effective annual yield, E, is the interest rate that would give the same amount of interest if the interest were compounded once per year. If P dollars are invested for one year, the value of the investment at the end of the year is $A = P(1 + E)$. If P dollars are invested for one year at a nominal rate r compounded n times per year, the value of the investment at the end of the year is $A = P\left(1 + \frac{r}{n}\right)^n$.

Setting the amounts equal and solving for E will produce a formula for the effective annual yield.

$$P(1 + E) = P\left(1 + \frac{r}{n}\right)^n$$
$$1 + E = \left(1 + \frac{r}{n}\right)^n$$
$$E = \left(1 + \frac{r}{n}\right)^n - 1$$

If compounding is continuous, the value of the investment at the end of one year is $A = Pe^r$. Again set the amounts equal and solve for E. A formula for the effective annual yield under continuous compounding is obtained.

$$P(1 + E) = Pe^r$$
$$1 + E = e^r$$
$$E = e^r - 1$$

Examples:

Find the effective annual yield of an investment made at 7.5% compounded monthly.

$r = 0.075$
$n = 12$
$E = \left(1 + \frac{0.075}{12}\right)^{12} - 1 \approx 7.76\%$

Find the effective annual yield of an investment made at 6.25% compounded continuously.

$r = 0.0625$
$E = e^{0.0625} - 1 \approx 6.45\%$

Find the effective annual yield for each investment.

1. 10% compounded quarterly
   10.38%

2. 8.5% compounded monthly
   8.84%

3. 9.25% compounded continuously
   9.69%

4. 7.75% compounded continuously
   8.06%

5. 6.5% compounded daily (assume a 365-day year)
   6.72%

6. Which investment yields more interest—9% compounded continuously or 9.2% compounded quarterly? **9.2% quarterly**

Enrichment

Families of Curves

Use these graphs for the problems below.

The Family $y = x^n$ The Family $y = e^{mx}$

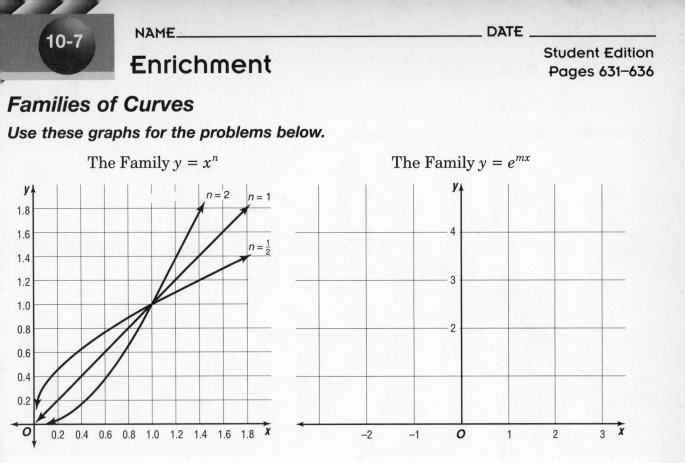

1. Use the graph on the left to describe the relationship among the curves $y = x^{\frac{1}{2}}$, $y = x^1$, and $y = x^2$.

2. Graph $y = x^n$ for $n = \dfrac{1}{10}, \dfrac{1}{4}$, 4, and 10 on the grid with $y = x^{\frac{1}{2}}$, $y = x^1$, and $y = x^2$.

3. Which two regions in the first quadrant contain no points of the graphs of the family for $y = x^n$?

4. On the right grid, graph the members of the family $y = e^{mx}$ for which $m = 1$ and $m = -1$.

5. Describe the relationship among these two curves and the y-axis.

6. Graph $y = e^{mx}$ for $m = 0, \pm\dfrac{1}{4}, \pm\dfrac{1}{2}, \pm2$, and ±4

Algebra 2

NAME_____ DATE _____

Enrichment

Student Edition
Pages 631–636

Families of Curves

Use these graphs for the problems below.

The Family $y = x^n$ The Family $y = e^{mx}$

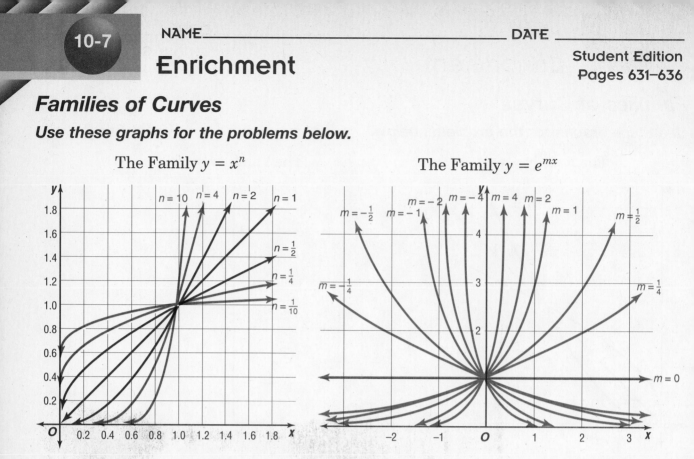

1. Use the graph on the left to describe the relationship among the curves $y = x^{\frac{1}{2}}$, $y = x^1$, and $y = x^2$. **For $n = \frac{1}{2}$ and $n = 2$, the graphs are reflections of one another in the line with equation $y = x^1$.**

2. Graph $y = x^n$ for $n = \frac{1}{10}, \frac{1}{4}, 4$, and 10 on the grid with $y = x^{\frac{1}{2}}$, $y = x^1$, and $y = x^2$. **See students' graphs.**

3. Which two regions in the first quadrant contain no points of the graphs of the family for $y = x^n$?
   $\{(x, y)|x \geq 1 \text{ and } 0 < y \leq 1\}$ **and** $\{(x, y)|0 < x \leq 1 \text{ and } y \geq 1\}$

4. On the right grid, graph the members of the family $y = e^{mx}$ for which $m = 1$ and $m = -1$. **See students' graphs.**

5. Describe the relationship among these two curves and the y-axis. **the graphs for $m = 1$ and $m = -1$ are reflections in the y-axis.**

6. Graph $y = e^{mx}$ for $m = 0, \pm\frac{1}{4}, \pm\frac{1}{2}, \pm2$, and ±4. **See students' graphs.**

Fibonacci Sequence

Leonardo Fibonacci first discovered the sequence of numbers named for him while studying rabbits. He wanted to know how many pairs of rabbits would be produced in n months, starting with a single pair of newborn rabbits. He made the following assumptions.

    1. Newborn rabbits become adults in one month.
    2. Each pair of rabbits produces one pair each month.
    3. No rabbits die.

Let F_n represent the number of pairs of rabbits at the end of n months. If you begin with one pair of newborn rabbits, $F_0 = F_1 = 1$. This pair of rabbits would produce one pair at the end of the second month, so $F_2 = 1 + 1$, or 2. At the end of the third month, the first pair of rabbits would produce another pair. Thus, $F_3 = 2 + 1$, or 3.

The chart below shows the number of rabbits each month for several months.

Month	Adult Pairs	Newborn Pairs	Total
F_0	0	1	1
F_1	1	0	1
F_2	1	1	2
F_3	2	1	3
F_4	3	2	5
F_5	5	3	8

Solve.

1. Starting with a single pair of newborn rabbits, how many rabbits would there be at the end of 12 months?

2. Write the first 10 terms of the sequence for which $F_0 = 3$, $F_1 = 4$, and $F_n = F_{n-2} + F_{n-1}$.

3. Write the first 10 terms of the sequence for which $F_0 = 1$, $F_1 = 5$, $F_n = F_{n-2} + F_{n-1}$.

Fibonacci Sequence

Leonardo Fibonacci first discovered the sequence of numbers named for him while studying rabbits. He wanted to know how many pairs of rabbits would be produced in n months, starting with a single pair of newborn rabbits. He made the following assumptions.

1. Newborn rabbits become adults in one month.
2. Each pair of rabbits produces one pair each month.
3. No rabbits die.

Let F_n represent the number of pairs of rabbits at the end of n months. If you begin with one pair of newborn rabbits, $F_0 = F_1 = 1$. This pair of rabbits would produce one pair at the end of the second month, so $F_2 = 1 + 1$, or 2. At the end of the third month, the first pair of rabbits would produce another pair. Thus, $F_3 = 2 + 1$, or 3.

The chart below shows the number of rabbits each month for several months.

Month	Adult Pairs	Newborn Pairs	Total
F_0	0	1	1
F_1	1	0	1
F_2	1	1	2
F_3	2	1	3
F_4	3	2	5
F_5	5	3	8

Solve.

1. Starting with a single pair of newborn rabbits, how many rabbits would there be at the end of 12 months? **233**

2. Write the first 10 terms of the sequence for which $F_0 = 3$, $F_1 = 4$, and $F_n = F_{n-2} + F_{n-1}$.
   3, 4, 7, 11, 18, 29, 47, 76, 123, 199, 322

3. Write the first 10 terms of the sequence for which $F_0 = 1$, $F_1 = 5$, $F_n = F_{n-2} + F_{n-1}$.
   1, 5, 6, 11, 17, 28, 45, 73, 118, 191, 309

Golden Rectangles

Use a straightedge, a compass, and the instructions below to construct a golden rectangle.

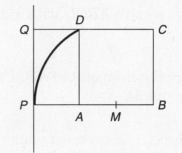

1. Construct square $ABCD$ with sides of 2 cm.

2. Construct the midpoint of $\overline{AB}$. Call the midpoint M.

3. Using M as the center, set your compass opening at MC. Construct an arc with center M that intersects $\overline{AB}$. Call the point of intersection P.

4. Construct a line through P that is perpendicular to $\overline{AB}$.

5. Extend $\overline{DC}$ so that it intersects the perpendicular. Call the intersection point Q. $APQD$ is a golden rectangle. Check this conclusion by finding the value of $\dfrac{QP}{AP}$.

A figure consisting of similar golden rectangles is shown below. Use a compass and the instructions below to draw quarter-circle arcs that form a spiral like that found in the shell of a chambered nautilus.

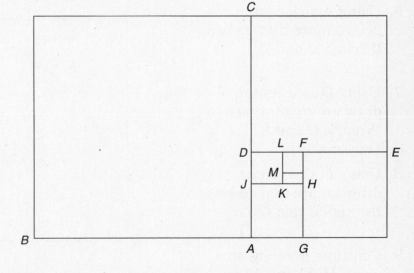

6. Using A as a center, draw an arc that passes through B and C.

7. Using D as a center, draw an arc that passes through C and E.

8. Using F as a center, draw an arc that passes through E and G.

9. Continue drawing arcs, using H, K, and M as the centers.

NAME_____ DATE _____

Enrichment

Golden Rectangles

Use a straightedge, a compass, and the instructions below to construct a golden rectangle.

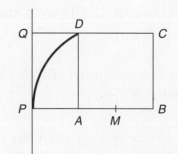

1. Construct square $ABCD$ with sides of 2 cm.

2. Construct the midpoint of $\overline{AB}$. Call the midpoint M.

3. Using M as the center, set your compass opening at MC. Construct an arc with center M that intersects $\overline{AB}$. Call the point of intersection P.

4. Construct a line through P that is perpendicular to $\overline{AB}$.

5. Extend $\overline{DC}$ so that it intersects the perpendicular. Call the intersection point Q. $APQD$ is a golden rectangle. Check this conclusion by finding the value of $\frac{QP}{AP}$. **0.62**

A figure consisting of similar golden rectangles is shown below. Use a compass and the instructions below to draw quarter-circle arcs that form a spiral like that found in the shell of a chambered nautilus.

6. Using A as a center, draw an arc that passes through B and C.

7. Using D as a center, draw an arc that passes through C and E.

8. Using F as a center, draw an arc that passes through E and G.

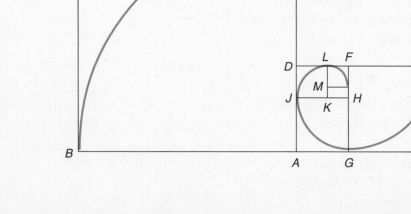

9. Continue drawing arcs, using H, K, and M as the centers.

NAME_____ DATE _____

Enrichment

Half the Distance

Suppose you are 200 feet from a fixed point, P. Suppose that you are able to move to the halfway point in one minute, to the next halfway point one minute after that, and so on.

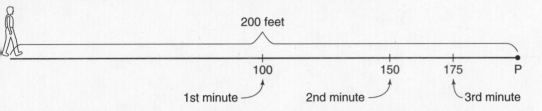

An interesting sequence results from this problem. According to the problem, you never actually reach the point P, but you do get arbitrarily close to it.

You can compute how long it will take to get within some specified small distance of the point. On a calculator, you enter the distance to be covered and then count the number of successive divisions by 2 necessary to get within the desired distance.

Example: How many minutes are needed to get within 0.1 feet of a point 200 feet away?

ENTER: 200 ÷ 2 = = = = = = = = = = =

Result: 0.0976562
Count the number of times pressing =.
The time needed is 11 minutes.

Use the method illustrated above to solve each problem.

1. If it is about 2500 miles from Los Angeles to New York, how many minutes would it take to get within 0.1 mile of New York? How far from New York are you at that time?

2. If it is 25,000 miles around Earth, how many minutes would it take to get within 0.5 mile of the full distance around Earth? How far short would you be?

3. If it is about 250,000 miles from Earth to the Moon, how many minutes would it take to get within 0.5 mile of the Moon? How far from the surface of the Moon would you be?

4. If it is about 30,000,000 feet from Honolulu to Miami, how many minutes would it take to get to within 1 foot of Miami? How far from Miami would you be at that time?

5. If it is about 93,000,000 miles to the sun, how many minutes would it take to get within 500 miles of the sun? How far from the sun would you be at that time?

Enrichment

Half the Distance

Suppose you are 200 feet from a fixed point, P. Suppose that
you are able to move to the halfway point in one minute, to the
next halfway point one minute after that, and so on.

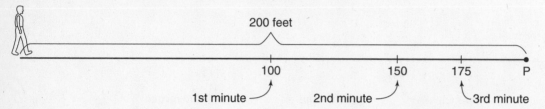

An interesting sequence results from this problem. According to
the problem, you never actually reach the point P, but you do
get arbitrarily close to it.

You can compute how long it will take to get within some specified
small distance of the point. On a calculator, you enter the distance
to be covered and then count the number of successive divisions
by 2 necessary to get within the desired distance.

Example: How many minutes are needed to get within 0.1 feet
of a point 200 feet away?

ENTER: 200 ÷ 2 = = = = = = = = = = =

Result: 0.0976562
Count the number of times pressing = .
The time needed is 11 minutes.

Use the method illustrated above to solve each problem.

1. If it is about 2500 miles from Los Angeles to New York, how
   many minutes would it take to get within 0.1 mile of New
   York? How far from New York are you at that time? **15 minutes, 0.0762934 mile**

2. If it is 25,000 miles around Earth, how many minutes would
   it take to get within 0.5 mile of the full distance around
   Earth? How far short would you be? **16 minutes; 0.3814697 mile**

3. If it is about 250,000 miles from Earth to the Moon, how many
   minutes would it take to get within 0.5 mile of the Moon? How
   far from the surface of the Moon would you be? **19 minutes, 0.4768372 mile**

4. If it is about 30,000,000 feet from Honolulu to Miami, how many
   minutes would it take to get to within 1 foot of Miami? How far
   from Miami would you be at that time? **25 minutes, 0.8940697 foot**

5. If it is about 93,000,000 miles to the sun, how many minutes
   would it take to get within 500 miles of the sun? How far from
   the sun would you be at that time? **18 minutes, 354.766846 miles**

Enrichment

Annuities

An annuity is a fixed amount of money payable at given intervals. For example, suppose you wanted to set up a trust fund so that $30,000 could be withdrawn each year for 14 years before the money ran out. Assume the money can be invested at 9%.

You must find the amount of money that needs to be invested. Call this amount A. After the third payment, the amount left is

$$1.09[1.09A - 30{,}000(1 + 1.09)] - 30{,}000 = 1.09^2 A - 30{,}000(1 + 1.09 + 1.09^2).$$

The results are summarized in the table below.

Payment Number	Number of Dollars Left After Payment
1	$A - 30{,}000$
2	$1.09A - 30{,}000(1 + 1.09)$
3	$1.09^2 A - 30{,}000(1 + 1.09 + 1.09^2)$

1. Use the pattern shown in the table to find the number of dollars left after the fourth payment.

2. Find the amount left after the tenth payment.

The amount left after the 14th payment is $1.09^{13}A - 30{,}000(1 + 1.09 + 1.09^2 + \cdots + 1.09^{13})$. However, there should be no money left after the 14th and final payment.

$$1.09^{13}A - 30{,}000(1 + 1.09 + 1.09^2 + \cdots + 1.09^{13}) = 0$$

Notice that $1 + 1.09 + 1.09^2 + \cdots + 1.09^{13}$ is a geometric series where $a_1 = 1$, $a_n = 1.09^{13}$, $n = 14$ and $r = 1.09$.

Using the formula for S_n,

$$1 + 1.09 + 1.09^2 + \cdots + 1.09^{13} = \frac{a_1 - a_1 r^n}{1 - r} = \frac{1 - 1.09^{14}}{1 - 1.09} = \frac{1 - 1.09^{14}}{-0.09}.$$

3. Show that when you solve for A you get $A = \dfrac{30{,}000}{0.09}\left(\dfrac{1.09^{14} - 1}{1.09^{13}}\right)$.

Therefore, to provide $30,000 for 14 years where the annual interest rate is 9%, you need $\dfrac{30{,}000}{0.09}\left(\dfrac{1.09^{14} - 1}{1.09^{13}}\right)$ dollars.

4. Use a calculator to find the value of A in problem 3.

In general, if you wish to provide P dollars for each of n years at an annual rate of $r\%$, you need A dollars where

$$\left(1 + \frac{r}{100}\right)^{n-1} A - P\left[1 + \left(1 + \frac{r}{100}\right) + \left(1 + \frac{r}{100}\right)^2 + \cdots + \left(1 + \frac{r}{100}\right)^{n-1}\right] = 0.$$

You can solve this equation for A, given P, n, and r.

Annuities

An annuity is a fixed amount of money payable at given intervals. For example, suppose you wanted to set up a trust fund so that $30,000 could be withdrawn each year for 14 years before the money ran out. Assume the money can be invested at 9%.

You must find the amount of money that needs to be invested. Call this amount A. After the third payment, the amount left is

$$1.09[1.09A - 30,000(1 + 1.09)] - 30,000 = 1.09^2A - 30,000(1 + 1.09 + 1.09^2).$$

The results are summarized in the table below.

Payment Number	Number of Dollars Left After Payment
1	$A - 30,000$
2	$1.09A - 30,000(1 + 1.09)$
3	$1.09^2A - 30,000(1 + 1.09 + 1.09^2)$

1. Use the pattern shown in the table to find the number of dollars left after the fourth payment.
   $1.09^3A - 30,000(1 + 1.09 + 1.09^2 + 1.09^3)$

2. Find the amount left after the tenth payment.

The amount left after the 14th payment is $1.09^{13}A - 30,000(1 + 1.09 + 1.09^2 + \cdots + 1.09^{13})$. However, there should be no money left after the 14th and final payment.

$$1.09^{13}A - 30,000(1 + 1.09 + 1.09^2 + \cdots + 1.09^{13}) = 0$$

Notice that $1 + 1.09 + 1.09^2 + \cdots + 1.09^{13}$ is a geometric series where $a_1 = 1$, $a_n = 1.09^{13}$, $n = 14$ and $r = 1.09$.

Using the formula for S_n,

$$1 + 1.09 + 1.09^2 + \cdots + 1.09^{13} = \frac{a_1 - a_1r^n}{1 - r} = \frac{1 - 1.09^{14}}{1 - 1.09} = \frac{1 - 1.09^{14}}{-0.09}.$$

3. Show that when you solve for A you get $A = \frac{30,000}{0.09}\left(\frac{1.09^{14} - 1}{1.09^{13}}\right)$.

   $1.09^{13}A - 30,000\left(\dfrac{1 - 1.09^{14}}{-0.09}\right) = 0$ results in stated expression for A.

Therefore, to provide $30,000 for 14 years where the annual interest rate is 9%, you need $\dfrac{30,000}{0.09}\left(\dfrac{1.09^{14} - 1}{1.09^{13}}\right)$ dollars.

4. Use a calculator to find the value of A in problem 3. $254,607

In general, if you wish to provide P dollars for each of n years at an annual rate of r%, you need A dollars where

$$\left(1 + \frac{r}{100}\right)^{n-1} A - P\left[1 + \left(1 + \frac{r}{100}\right) + \left(1 + \frac{r}{100}\right)^2 + \cdots + \left(1 + \frac{r}{100}\right)^{n-1}\right] = 0.$$

You can solve this equation for A, given P, n, and r.

Enrichment

Convergence and Divergence

Convergence and divergence are terms that relate to the existence of a sum of an infinite series. If a sum exists, the series is convergent. If not, the series is divergent. Consider the series $12 + 3 + \frac{3}{4} + \frac{3}{16} + \cdots$. This is a geometric series with $r = \frac{1}{4}$. The sum is given by the formula $S = \frac{a_1}{1 - r}$. Thus, the sum is $12 \div \frac{3}{4}$ or 16. This series is convergent since a sum exists. Notice that the first two terms have a sum of 15. As more terms are added, the sum comes closer (or converges) to 16.

Recall that a geometric series has a sum if and only if $-1 < r < 1$. Thus, a geometric series is convergent if r is between -1 and 1, and divergent if r has another value. An infinite arithmetic series cannot have a sum unless all of the terms are equal to zero.

Examples: (a) $2 + 5 + 8 + 11 + \cdots$ divergent

(b) $-2 + 4 + -8 + 16 + \cdots$ divergent

(c) $16 + 8 + 4 + 2 + \cdots$ convergent

Determine whether each series is convergent or divergent. If the series is convergent, find the sum.

1. $5 + 10 + 15 + 20 + \cdots$

2. $16 + 8 + 4 + 2 + \cdots$

3. $1 + 0.1 + 0.01 + 0.001 + \cdots$

4. $4 + 2 + 0 - 2 - \cdots$

5. $2 - 4 + 8 - 16 + \cdots$

6. $1 - \frac{1}{5} + \frac{1}{25} - \frac{1}{125} + \cdots$

7. $4 + 2.4 + 1.44 + 0.864 + \cdots$

8. $\frac{1}{8} + \frac{1}{4} + \frac{1}{2} + 1 + \cdots$

9. $-\frac{5}{3} + \frac{10}{9} - \frac{20}{27} + \frac{40}{81} - \cdots$

10. $48 + 12 + 3 + \frac{3}{4} + \cdots$

Bonus: Is $1 + \frac{1}{2} + \frac{1}{3} + \frac{1}{4} + \frac{1}{5} + \cdots$ convergent or divergent?

Convergence and Divergence

Convergence and divergence are terms that relate to the existence of a sum of an infinite series. If a sum exists, the series is convergent. If not, the series is divergent. Consider the series $12 + 3 + \frac{3}{4} + \frac{3}{16} + \cdots$. This is a geometric series with $r = \frac{1}{4}$. The sum is given by the formula $S = \frac{a_1}{1 - r}$. Thus, the sum is $12 \div \frac{3}{4}$ or 16. This series is convergent since a sum exists. Notice that the first two terms have a sum of 15. As more terms are added, the sum comes closer (or converges) to 16.

Recall that a geometric series has a sum if and only if $-1 < r < 1$. Thus, a geometric series is convergent if r is between -1 and 1, and divergent if r has another value. An infinite arithmetic series cannot have a sum unless all of the terms are equal to zero.

Examples: (a) $2 + 5 + 8 + 11 + \cdots$ divergent

(b) $-2 + 4 + -8 + 16 + \cdots$ divergent

(c) $16 + 8 + 4 + 2 + \cdots$ convergent

Determine whether each series is convergent or divergent. If the series is convergent, find the sum.

1. $5 + 10 + 15 + 20 + \cdots$
   divergent

2. $16 + 8 + 4 + 2 + \cdots$
   convergent; 32

3. $1 + 0.1 + 0.01 + 0.001 + \cdots$
   convergent; 1.11

4. $4 + 2 + 0 - 2 - \cdots$
   divergent

5. $2 - 4 + 8 - 16 + \cdots$
   divergent

6. $1 - \frac{1}{5} + \frac{1}{25} - \frac{1}{125} + \cdots$
   convergent; $\frac{5}{6}$

7. $4 + 2.4 + 1.44 + 0.864 + \cdots$
   convergent; 10

8. $\frac{1}{8} + \frac{1}{4} + \frac{1}{2} + 1 + \cdots$
   divergent

9. $-\frac{5}{3} + \frac{10}{9} - \frac{20}{27} + \frac{40}{81} - \cdots$
   convergent; -1

10. $48 + 12 + 3 + \frac{3}{4} + \cdots$
    convergent; 64

Bonus: Is $1 + \frac{1}{2} + \frac{1}{3} + \frac{1}{4} + \frac{1}{5} + \cdots$ convergent or divergent?
divergent

Algebra 2

Enrichment

Quadratic Formulas for Sequences

An ordinary arithmetic sequence is formed using a rule such as $bn + c$. The first term is c, b is called the common difference, and n takes on the values 0, 1, 2, 3, and so on. The value of term $n + 1$ equals $b(n + 1) + c$ or $bn + b + c$. So, the value of a term is a function of the term number.

Some sequences use quadratic functions. A method called *finite differences* can be used to find the values of the terms. Notice what happens when you subtract twice as shown in this table.

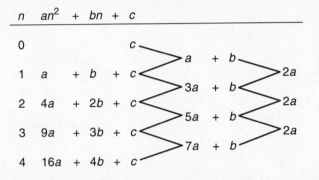

n	$an^2 + bn + c$
0	c
1	$a + b + c$
2	$4a + 2b + c$
3	$9a + 3b + c$
4	$16a + 4b + c$

A sequence that yields a common difference after two subtractions can be generated by a quadratic expression. For example, the sequence 1, 5, 12, 22, 35, ⋯ gives a common difference of 3 after two subtractions. Using the table above, you write and solve three equations to find the general rule. The equations are $1 = c$, $5 = a + b + c$, and $12 = 4a + 2b + c$.

Solve each problem.

1. Refer to the sequence in the example above. Solve the system of equations for a, b, and c and then find the quadratic expression for the sequence. Then write the next three terms.

2. The number of line segments connecting n points forms the sequence 0, 0, 1, 3, 6, 10, ⋯, in which n is the number of points and the term value is the number of line segments. What is the common difference after the second subtraction? Find a quadratic expression for the term value.

3. The maximum number of regions formed by n chords in a circle forms the sequence 1, 2, 4, 7, 11, 16, ⋯. (A chord is a line segment joining any two points on a circle.) Draw circles to illustrate the first four terms of the sequence. Then find a quadratic expression for the term value.

Algebra 2

Enrichment

Quadratic Formulas for Sequences

An ordinary arithmetic sequence is formed using a rule such as $bn + c$. The first term is c, b is called the common difference, and n takes on the values 0, 1, 2, 3, and so on. The value of term $n + 1$ equals $b(n + 1) + c$ or $bn + b + c$. So, the value of a term is a function of the term number.

Some sequences use quadratic functions. A method called *finite differences* can be used to find the values of the terms. Notice what happens when you subtract twice as shown in this table.

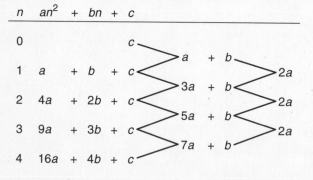

A sequence that yields a common difference after two subtractions can be generated by a quadratic expression. For example, the sequence 1, 5, 12, 22, 35, ⋯ gives a common difference of 3 after two subtractions. Using the table above, you write and solve three equations to find the general rule. The equations are $1 = c$, $5 = a + b + c$, and $12 = 4a + 2b + c$.

Solve each problem.

1. Refer to the sequence in the example above. Solve the system of equations for a, b, and c and then find the quadratic expression for the sequence. Then write the next three terms.
$\frac{3}{2}n^2 + \frac{5}{2}n + 1$; **51, 70, 92**

2. The number of line segments connecting n points forms the sequence 0, 0, 1, 3, 6, 10, ⋯, in which n is the number of points and the term value is the number of line segments. What is the common difference after the second subtraction? Find a quadratic expression for the term value.
1; $\frac{1}{2}n^2 - \frac{1}{2}n$

3. The maximum number of regions formed by n chords in a circle forms the sequence 1, 2, 4, 7, 11, 16, ⋯. (A chord is a line segment joining any two points on a circle.) Draw circles to illustrate the first four terms of the sequence. Then find a quadratic expression for the term value.

$\frac{1}{2}n^2 + \frac{1}{2}n + 1$

Algebra 2

NAME_____ DATE _____

Enrichment

Student Edition
Pages 688–694

Geometric Puzzlers

For the problems on this page, you will need to use the Pythagorean Theorem and the formulas for the area of a triangle and a trapezoid.

1. A rectangle measures 5 by 12 units. The upper left corner is cut off as shown in the diagram.

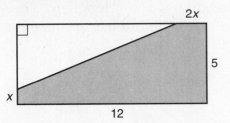

a. Find the area $A(x)$ of the shaded pentagon.

b. Find x and $2x$ so that $A(x)$ is a maximum. What happens to the cut-off triangle?

2. A triangle with sides of lengths a, a, and b is isosceles. Two triangles are cut off so that the remaining pentagon has five equal sides of length x. The value of x can be found using this equation.

$$(2b - a)x^2 + (4a^2 - b^2)(2x - a) = 0$$

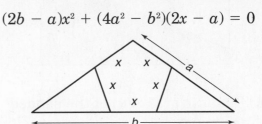

a. Find x when $a = 10$ and $b = 12$.

b. Can a be equal to $2b$?

3. The coordinates of the vertices of a triangle are $A(0, 0)$, $B(11, 0)$, and $C(0, 11)$. A line $x = k$ cuts the triangle into two equal pieces having equal area.

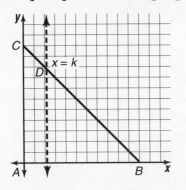

a. What are the coordinates of point D?

b. Write and solve an equation for finding the value of k.

4. Inside a square are five circles with the same radius.

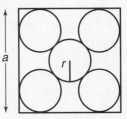

a. Connect the center of the top left circle to the center of the bottom right circle. Express this length in terms of r.

b. Draw the square with vertices at the centers of the four outside circles. Express the diagonal of this square in terms of r and a.

Algebra 2

Geometric Puzzlers

For the problems on this page, you will need to use the Pythagorean Theorem and the formulas for the area of a triangle and a trapezoid.

1. A rectangle measures 5 by 12 units. The upper left corner is cut off as shown in the diagram.

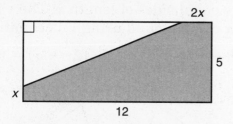

a. Find the area $A(x)$ of the shaded pentagon.
$A(x) = 60 - (5 - x)(6 - x)$

b. Find x and $2x$ so that $A(x)$ is a maximum. What happens to the cut-off triangle?
$x = 5$ and $2x = 10$; the triangle will not exist.

2. A triangle with sides of lengths a, a, and b is isosceles. Two triangles are cut off so that the remaining pentagon has five equal sides of length x. The value of x can be found using this equation.

$$(2b - a)x^2 + (4a^2 - b^2)(2x - a) = 0$$

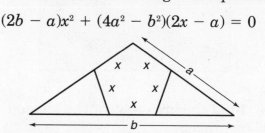

a. Find x when $a = 10$ and $b = 12$.
$x \approx 4.46$

b. Can a be equal to $2b$?
Yes, but it would not be possible to have a pentagon of the type described.

3. The coordinates of the vertices of a triangle are $A(0, 0)$, $B(11, 0)$, and $C(0, 11)$. A line $x = k$ cuts the triangle into two equal pieces having equal area.

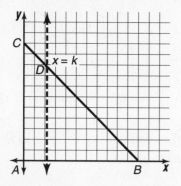

a. What are the coordinates of point D?
$(k, 11 - k)$

b. Write and solve an equation for finding the value of k.
$\frac{1}{2}k(11 + 11 - k) = 22$;
$k = 11 - \sqrt{77}$

4. Inside a square are five circles with the same radius.

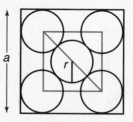

a. Connect the center of the top left circle to the center of the bottom right circle. Express this length in terms of r.
4r

b. Draw the square with vertices at the centers of the four outside circles. Express the diagonal of this square in terms of r and a.
$(a - 2r)\sqrt{2}$

Enrichment

Patterns in Pascal's Triangle

You have learned that the coefficients in the expansion of $(x + y)^n$ yield a number pyramid called **Pascal's triangle.**

Row 1 ⟶ 1
Row 2 ⟶ 1 1
Row 3 ⟶ 1 2 1
Row 4 ⟶ 1 3 3 1
Row 5 ⟶ 1 4 6 4 1
Row 6 ⟶ 1 5 10 10 5 1
Row 7 ⟶ 1 6 15 20 15 6 1

As many rows can be added to the bottom of the pyramid as you please.

This activity explores some of the interesting properties of this famous number pyramid.

1. Pick a row of Pascal's triangle.
   a. What is the sum of all the numbers in all the rows *above* the row you picked?
   b. What is the sum of all the numbers in the row you picked?
   c. How are your answers for parts a and b related?

   d. Repeat Parts a through c for at least three more rows of Pascal's triangle. What generalization seems to be true?

   e. See if you can prove your generalization.

2. Pick any row of Pascal's triangle that comes after the first.
   a. Starting at the left end of the row, add the first number, the third number, the fifth number, and so on. State the sum.
   b. In the same row, add the second number, the fourth number, and so on. State the sum.
   c. How do the sums in Parts a and b compare?
   d. Repeat Parts a through c for at least three other rows of Pascal's triangle. What generalization seems to be true?

NAME_____ DATE _____

Enrichment

Patterns in Pascal's Triangle

You have learned that the coefficients in the expansion of $(x + y)^n$ yield a number pyramid called **Pascal's triangle.**

Row 1 ⟶	1
Row 2 ⟶	1 1
Row 3 ⟶	1 2 1
Row 4 ⟶	1 3 3 1
Row 5 ⟶	1 4 6 4 1
Row 6 ⟶	1 5 10 10 5 1
Row 7 ⟶	1 6 15 20 15 6 1

As many rows can be added to the bottom of the pyramid as you please.

This activity explores some of the interesting properties of this famous number pyramid.

1. Pick a row of Pascal's triangle.
   a. What is the sum of all the numbers in all the rows *above* the row you picked? **See students' work.**
   b. What is the sum of all the numbers in the row you picked? **See students' work.**
   c. How are your answers for parts a and b related? **The answer for Part b is 1 more than the answer for Part a.**
   d. Repeat Parts a through c for at least three more rows of Pascal's triangle. What generalization seems to be true? **It appears that the sum of the numbers in any row is 1 more than the sum of the numbers in all of the rows above it.**
   e. See if you can prove your generalization. **Sum of numbers in row $n = 2^n - 1$; $2^0 + 2^1 + 2^2 + \cdots + 2^{n-2}$, which, by the formula for the sum of a geometric series, is $2^{n-1} - 1$.**

2. Pick any row of Pascal's triangle that comes after the first.
   a. Starting at the left end of the row, add the first number, the third number, the fifth number, and so on. State the sum. **See students' work.**
   b. In the same row, add the second number, the fourth number, and so on. State the sum. **See students' work.**
   c. How do the sums in Parts a and b compare? **The sums are equal.**
   d. Repeat Parts a through c for at least three other rows of Pascal's triangle. What generalization seems to be true? **In any row of Pascal's triangle after the first, the sum of the odd numbered terms is equal to the sum of the even numbered terms.**

Tree Diagrams and the Power Rule

If you flip a coin once, there are two possible outcomes: heads showing (H) or tails showing (T). The tree diagram to the right shows the four (2^2) possible outcomes if you flip a coin twice.

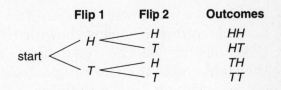

Example 1: Draw a tree diagram to show all the possible outcomes for flipping a coin three times. List the outcomes.

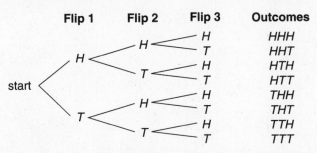

There are eight (2^3) possible outcomes. With each extra flip, the number of outcomes doubles. With 4 flips, there would be sixteen (2^4) outcomes.

Example 2: In a cup there are a red, a blue, and a yellow marble. How many possible outcomes are there if you draw one marble at random, replace it, and then draw another?

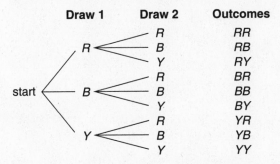

There are nine (3^2) possible outcomes.

The Power Rule for the number of outcomes states that if an experiment is repeated n times, and if there are b possible outcomes each time, there are b^n total possible outcomes.

Find the total number of possible outcomes for each experiment. Use tree diagrams to help you.

1. flipping a coin 5 times

2. doing the marble experiment 6 times

3. flipping a coin 8 times

4. rolling a 6-sided die 2 times

5. rolling a 6-sided die 3 times

6. rolling a 4-sided die 2 times

7. rolling a 4-sided die 3 times

8. rolling a 12-sided die 2 times

Enrichment

Tree Diagrams and the Power Rule

If you flip a coin once, there are two possible outcomes: heads showing (H) or tails showing (T). The tree diagram to the right shows the four (2^2) possible outcomes if you flip a coin twice.

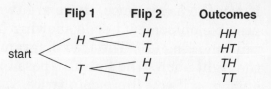

Example 1: Draw a tree diagram to show all the possible outcomes for flipping a coin three times. List the outcomes.

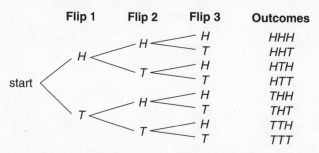

There are eight (2^3) possible outcomes. With each extra flip, the number of outcomes doubles. With 4 flips, there would be sixteen (2^4) outcomes.

Example 2: In a cup there are a red, a blue, and a yellow marble. How many possible outcomes are there if you draw one marble at random, replace it, and then draw another?

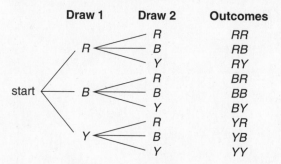

There are nine (3^2) possible outcomes.

The Power Rule for the number of outcomes states that if an experiment is repeated n times, and if there are b possible outcomes each time, there are b^n total possible outcomes.

Find the total number of possible outcomes for each experiment. Use tree diagrams to help you.

1. flipping a coin 5 times 2^5

2. doing the marble experiment 6 times 3^6

3. flipping a coin 8 times 2^8

4. rolling a 6-sided die 2 times 6^2

5. rolling a 6-sided die 3 times 6^3

6. rolling a 4-sided die 2 times 4^2

7. rolling a 4-sided die 3 times 4^3

8. rolling a 12-sided die 2 times 12^2

Enrichment

Street Networks: Finding All Possible Routes

A section of a city is laid out in square blocks. Going north from the intersection of First Avenue and First Street, the avenues are 1st, 2nd, 3rd, and so on. Going east, the streets are numbered in the same way.

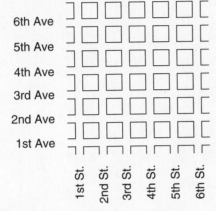

6th Ave
5th Ave
4th Ave
3rd Ave
2nd Ave
1st Ave

1st St. 2nd St. 3rd St. 4th St. 5th St. 6th St.

Factorials can be used to find the number, $r(e, n)$, of different routes between two intersections. The formula is shown at the right. The number of streets going east is e; the number of avenues going north is n.

$$r(e, n) = \frac{[(e - 1) + (n - 1)]!}{(e - 1)! \, (n - 1)!}$$

The following problems examine the possible routes from one location to another. Assume that you never use a route that is unnecessarily long. Assume that $e \geq 1$ and $n \geq 1$.

Solve each problem.

1. List all the possible routes from 1st Street and 1st Avenue to 4th Street and 3rd Avenue. Use ordered pairs to show the routes, with street numbers first, and avenue numbers second. For example, each route starts at (1, 1) and ends at (4, 3).

2. Use the formula to compute the number of routes from (1, 1) to (4, 3). There are 4 streets going east and 3 avenues going north.

3. Find the number of routes from 1st Street and 1st Avenue to 7th Street and 6th Avenue.

Enrichment

Street Networks: Finding All Possible Routes

A section of a city is laid out in square blocks. Going north from the intersection of First Avenue and First Street, the avenues are 1st, 2nd, 3rd, and so on. Going east, the streets are numbered in the same way.

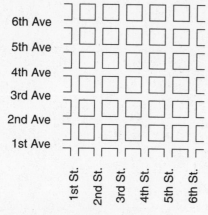

Factorials can be used to find the number, $r(e, n)$, of different routes between two intersections. The formula is shown at the right. The number of streets going east is e; the number of avenues going north is n.

$$r(e, n) = \frac{[(e - 1) + (n - 1)]!}{(e - 1)! \, (n - 1)!}$$

The following problems examine the possible routes from one location to another. Assume that you never use a route that is unnecessarily long. Assume that $e \geq 1$ and $n \geq 1$.

Solve each problem.

1. List all the possible routes from 1st Street and 1st Avenue to 4th Street and 3rd Avenue. Use ordered pairs to show the routes, with street numbers first, and avenue numbers second. For example, each route starts at (1, 1) and ends at (4, 3).

   (1, 1) − (2, 1) − (3, 1) − (4, 1) − (4, 2) − (4, 3)
   (1, 1) − (2, 1) − (3, 1) − (3, 2) − (4, 2) − (4, 3)
   (1, 1) − (2, 1) − (3, 1) − (3, 2) − (3, 3) − (4, 3)
   (1, 1) − (2, 1) − (2, 2) − (3, 2) − (4, 2) − (4, 3)
   (1, 1) − (2, 1) − (2, 2) − (3, 2) − (3, 3) − (4, 3)
   (1, 1) − (2, 1) − (2, 2) − (2, 3) − (3, 3) − (4, 3)
   (1, 1) − (1, 2) − (2, 2) − (3, 2) − (4, 2) − (4, 3)
   (1, 1) − (1, 2) − (2, 2) − (3, 2) − (3, 3) − (4, 3)
   (1, 1) − (1, 2) − (2, 2) − (2, 3) − (3, 3) − (4, 3)
   (1, 1) − (1, 2) − (1, 3) − (2, 3) − (3, 3) − (4, 3)

2. Use the formula to compute the number of routes from (1, 1) to (4, 3). There are 4 streets going east and 3 avenues going north. $\dfrac{(3 + 2)!}{3!2!} = 10$

3. Find the number of routes from 1st Street and 1st Avenue to 7th Street and 6th Avenue. $\dfrac{(6 + 5)!}{6!5!} = 462$

Enrichment

Student Edition
Pages 726–731

Combinations and Pascal's Triangle

Pascal's triangle is a special array of numbers invented by
Blaise Pascal (1623–1662). The values in Pascal's triangle can
be found using the combinations shown below.

1. Evaluate the expression in each cell of the triangle.

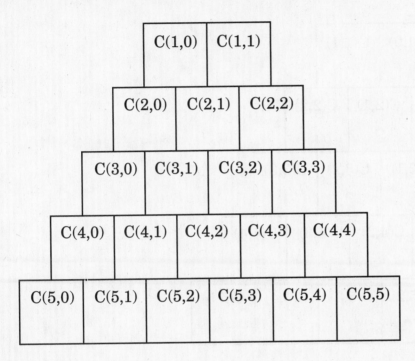

2. The pattern shows the relationship between $C(n, r)$ and
Pascal's triangle. In general, it is true that $C(n, r) +
C(n, r + 1) = C(n + 1, r + 1)$. Complete the proof of this
property. In each step, the denominator has been given.

$$C(n, r) + C(n, r + 1) = \frac{}{r!(n - r)!} + \frac{}{(r + 1)!(n - r - 1)!}$$

$$= \frac{}{r!(n - r)!(r + 1)} + \frac{}{(r + 1)!(n - r - 1)!(n - r)}$$

$$= \frac{}{(r + 1)!(n - r)!} + \frac{}{(r + 1)!(n - r)!}$$

$$= \frac{}{(r + 1)!(n - r)!}$$

$$= \frac{}{(r + 1)!(n - r)!}$$

$$= \frac{}{(r + 1)!(n - r)!}$$

$$= \frac{}{(r + 1)![(n + 1) - (r + 1)]!}$$

$$= C(n + 1, r + 1)$$

Enrichment

Combinations and Pascal's Triangle

Pascal's triangle is a special array of numbers invented by
Blaise Pascal (1623–1662). The values in Pascal's triangle can
be found using the combinations shown below.

1. Evaluate the expression in each cell of the triangle.

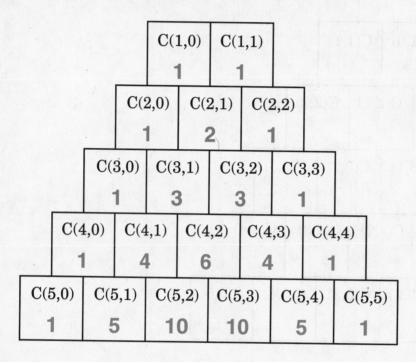

2. The pattern shows the relationship between $C(n, r)$ and
Pascal's triangle. In general, it is true that $C(n, r) +
C(n, r + 1) = C(n + 1, r + 1)$. Complete the proof of this
property. In each step, the denominator has been given.

$$C(n, r) + C(n, r + 1) = \frac{n!}{r!(n - r)!} + \frac{n!}{(r + 1)!(n - r - 1)!}$$

$$= \frac{n!(r + 1)}{r!(n - r)!(r + 1)} + \frac{n!(n - r)}{(r + 1)!(n - r - 1)!(n - r)}$$

$$= \frac{n!(r + 1)}{(r + 1)!(n - r)!} + \frac{n!(n - r)}{(r + 1)!(n - r)!}$$

$$= \frac{n!(r + 1 + n - r)}{(r + 1)!(n - r)!}$$

$$= \frac{n!(n + 1)}{(r + 1)!(n - r)!}$$

$$= \frac{(n + 1)!}{(r + 1)!(n - r)!}$$

$$= \frac{(n + 1)!}{(r + 1)![(n + 1) - (r + 1)]!}$$

$$= C(n + 1, r + 1)$$

Algebra 2

NAME _____ DATE _____

Enrichment

Geometric Probability

If a dart, thrown at random, hits the
triangular board shown at the right,
what is the chance that it will hit the
shaded region? This chance, also called
a probability, can be determined by
comparing the area of the shaded region
to the area of the board. This ratio
indicates what fraction of the tosses
should hit in the shaded region.

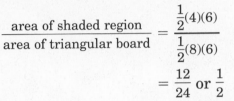

$$\frac{\text{area of shaded region}}{\text{area of triangular board}} = \frac{\frac{1}{2}(4)(6)}{\frac{1}{2}(8)(6)}$$

$$= \frac{12}{24} \text{ or } \frac{1}{2}$$

In general, if S is a subregion of some region R, then the
probability, $P(S)$, that a point, chosen at random, belongs to
subregion S is given by the following.

$$P(S) = \frac{\text{area of subregion } S}{\text{area of region } R}$$

**Find the probability that a point, chosen at random, belongs
to the shaded subregions of the following regions.**

1.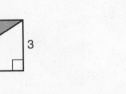

2.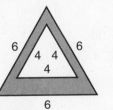

3.

**The dart board shown at the right has
5 concentric circles whose centers are
also the center of the square board.
Each side of the board is 38 cm, and
the radii of the circles are 2 cm, 5 cm,
8 cm, 11 cm, and 14 cm. A dart hitting
within one of the circular regions
scores the number of points indicated
on the board, while a hit anywhere else
scores 0 points.**

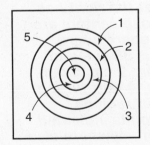

**If a dart, thrown at random, hits the board, find the probability
of scoring the indicated number of points.**

4. 0 points

5. 1 point

6. 2 points

7. 3 points

8. 4 points

9. 5 points

Algebra 2

NAME_____ DATE _____

Enrichment

Geometric Probability

If a dart, thrown at random, hits the
triangular board shown at the right,
what is the chance that it will hit the
shaded region? This chance, also called
a probability, can be determined by
comparing the area of the shaded region
to the area of the board. This ratio
indicates what fraction of the tosses
should hit in the shaded region.

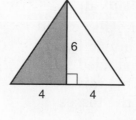

$$\frac{\text{area of shaded region}}{\text{area of triangular board}} = \frac{\frac{1}{2}(4)(6)}{\frac{1}{2}(8)(6)}$$

$$= \frac{12}{24} \text{ or } \frac{1}{2}$$

In general, if S is a subregion of some region R, then the
probability, $P(S)$, that a point, chosen at random, belongs to
subregion S is given by the following.

$$P(S) = \frac{\text{area of subregion } S}{\text{area of region } R}$$

**Find the probability that a point, chosen at random, belongs
to the shaded subregions of the following regions.**

1. 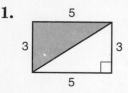 $\dfrac{1}{2}$

2. 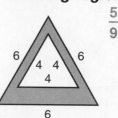 $\dfrac{5}{9}$

3. 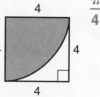 $\dfrac{\pi}{4}$

**The dart board shown at the right has
5 concentric circles whose centers are
also the center of the square board.
Each side of the board is 38 cm, and
the radii of the circles are 2 cm, 5 cm,
8 cm, 11 cm, and 14 cm. A dart hitting
within one of the circular regions
scores the number of points indicated
on the board, while a hit anywhere else
scores 0 points.**

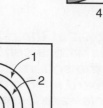

**If a dart, thrown at random, hits the board, find the probability
of scoring the indicated number of points.**

4. 0 points $\dfrac{361 - 49\pi}{361}$

5. 1 point $\dfrac{75\pi}{1444}$

6. 2 points $\dfrac{57\pi}{1444}$

7. 3 points $\dfrac{39\pi}{1444}$

8. 4 points $\dfrac{21\pi}{1444}$

9. 5 points $\dfrac{\pi}{361}$

Algebra 2

Enrichment

Probabilities in Genetics

Genes are the units which transmit hereditary traits. The possible forms which a gene may take, **dominant** and **recessive,** are called **alleles.** A particular trait is determined by two alleles, one from the female parent and one from the male parent. If an organism has the trait which is dominant, it may have either two dominant alleles or one dominant and one recessive allele. If the organism has the trait which is recessive, it must have two recessive alleles.

Example: Consider a plant in which tall stems, T, are dominant to short stems, t. What is the probability of obtaining a long-stemmed plant if two long-stemmed plants both with the genetic formula Tt are crossed?

	T	t
T	TT	Tt
t	Tt	tt

A *Punnett square* is a chart used to determine the possible combinations of characteristics among offspring.

$$\begin{array}{l} \text{3 tall-stemmed} \\ + \text{1 short-stemmed} \\ \hline \text{4 total} \end{array}$$

Thus, the probability is $\frac{3}{4}$.

In a certain plant, red flowers, R, are dominant to white flowers, r. If a white-flowered plant, rr is crossed with a red-flowered plant, Rr, find the probability of each of the following.

1. white-flowered plant

2. red-flowered plant

In a certain plant, tall, T, is dominant to short, t, and green pods, G, are dominant to yellow pods, g. Plants with the genetic formulas TtGg and TTGg are crossed. Find the probability of each of the following.

3. tall plant with green pods

4. tall plant with yellow pods

Probabilities in Genetics

Genes are the units which transmit hereditary traits. The possible forms which a gene may take, **dominant** and **recessive,** are called **alleles.** A particular trait is determined by two alleles, one from the female parent and one from the male parent. If an organism has the trait which is dominant, it may have either two dominant alleles or one dominant and one recessive allele. If the organism has the trait which is recessive, it must have two recessive alleles.

Example: Consider a plant in which tall stems, T, are dominant to short stems, t. What is the probability of obtaining a long-stemmed plant if two long-stemmed plants both with the genetic formula Tt are crossed?

	T	t
T	TT	Tt
t	Tt	tt

A *Punnett square* is a chart used to determine the possible combinations of characteristics among offspring.

$$\begin{array}{r} 3 \text{ tall-stemmed} \\ + 1 \text{ short-stemmed} \\ \hline 4 \text{ total} \end{array}$$

Thus, the probability is $\frac{3}{4}$.

In a certain plant, red flowers, R, are dominant to white flowers, r. If a white-flowered plant, rr is crossed with a red-flowered plant, Rr, find the probability of each of the following.

1. white-flowered plant $\frac{1}{2}$

2. red-flowered plant $\frac{1}{2}$

In a certain plant, tall, T, is dominant to short, t, and green pods, G, are dominant to yellow pods, g. Plants with the genetic formulas TtGg and TTGg are crossed. Find the probability of each of the following.

3. tall plant with green pods $\frac{3}{4}$

4. tall plant with yellow pods $\frac{1}{4}$

NAME_____ DATE _____

Enrichment

Probability and Tic-Tac-Toe

What would be the chances of winning at tic-tac-toe if it were turned into a game of pure chance? To find out, the nine cells of the tic-tac-toe board are numbered from 1 to 9 and nine chips (also numbered from 1 to 9) are put into a bag. Player A draws a chip at random and enters an X in the corresponding cell. Player B does the same and enters an O.

To solve the problem, assume that both players draw all their chips without looking and all X and O entries are made at the same time. There are four possible outcomes: a draw, A wins, B wins, and either A or B can win.

There are 16 arrangements that result in a draw. Reflections and rotations must be counted as shown below.

```
O X O        X O X        O O X
X O X  4     O O X  4     X X O  8
X O X        X X O        O X X
```

There are 36 arrangements in which either player may win because both players have winning triples.

```
X X X        X X X        X O X        X X X        X X X        X X O
O O O  4     X O X  4     X X X  4     X X O  8     O O O  8     X X X  8
X O X        O O O        O O O        O O O        X X O        O O O
```

In these 36 cases, A's chances of winning are $\frac{13}{40}$.

1. Find the 12 arrangements in which B wins and A cannot.

2. Below are 12 of the arrangements in which A wins and B cannot. Write the numbers to show the reflections and rotations for each arrangement. What is the total number?

```
O X O    X O X    X X X    X X X    X O O    X O O
X X X    O X O    X O O    O X O    X X X    X X O
O X O    X O X    X O O    O X O    O O X    O O X

X X O    X X X    X X X    X X X    X O O    X X O
O X X    O X O    X O O    X O O    X X X    O X O
O O X    O O X    O X O    O O X    O X O    X O X
```

3. There are $\frac{9!}{(5!4!)}$ different and equally probable distributions. Complete the chart to find the probability for a draw or for A or B to win.

Draw:	$\frac{16}{126}$	= _____
A wins:	_____ + $\frac{13}{40}\left(\frac{36}{126}\right)$	= _____
B wins:	_____ + _____	= _____

NAME_____ DATE _____

Enrichment

Probability and Tic-Tac-Toe

What would be the chances of winning at tic-tac-toe if it were turned into a game of pure chance? To find out, the nine cells of the tic-tac-toe board are numbered from 1 to 9 and nine chips (also numbered from 1 to 9) are put into a bag. Player A draws a chip at random and enters an X in the corresponding cell. Player B does the same and enters an O.

To solve the problem, assume that both players draw all their chips without looking and all X and O entries are made at the same time. There are four possible outcomes: a draw, A wins, B wins, and either A or B can win.

There are 16 arrangements that result in a draw. Reflections and rotations must be counted as shown below.

```
o x o        x o x        o o x
x o x  4      o o x  4      x x o  8
x o x        x x o        o x x
```

There are 36 arrangements in which either player may win because both players have winning triples.

```
x x x     x x x     x o x     x x x     x x x     x x o
o o o  4   x o x  4   x x x  4   x x o  8   o o o  8   x x x  8
x o x     o o o     o o o     o o o     x x o     o o o
```

In these 36 cases, A's chances of winning are $\frac{13}{40}$.

1. Find the 12 arrangements in which B wins and A cannot.

```
o o x        o x o
x o x  8      x o x  4
x x o        x x o
```

2. Below are 12 of the arrangements in which A wins and B cannot. Write the numbers to show the reflections and rotations for each arrangement. What is the total number? **62**

```
o x o        x o x        x x x        x x x        x o o        x o o
x x x  1      o x o  1      x o o  4      o x o  4      x x x  4      x x o  4
o x o        x o x        x o o        o x o        o o x        o o x

x x o        x x x        x x x        x x x        x o o        x x o
o x x  4      o x o  8      x o o  8      x o o  8      x x x  8      o x o  8
o o x        o o x        o x o        o o x        o x o        x o x
```

3. There are $\dfrac{9!}{(5!4!)}$ different and equally probable distributions. Complete the chart to find the probability for a draw or for A or B to win.

Draw: $\dfrac{16}{126}$		$= \dfrac{8}{63}$
A wins: $\dfrac{62}{126}$	$+ \dfrac{13}{40}\left(\dfrac{36}{126}\right)$	$= \dfrac{737}{1260}$
B wins: $\dfrac{12}{126}$	$+ \dfrac{27}{40}\left(\dfrac{36}{126}\right)$	$= \dfrac{121}{420}$

NAME_____ DATE _____

Enrichment

Conditional Probability

Suppose a pair of dice is thrown. It is known that the sum is greater than seven. Find the probability that the dice match.

The probability of an event given the occurrence of another event is called *conditional probability*. The conditional probability of event A, the dice match, given event B, their sum is greater than seven, is denoted $P(A/B)$.

There are 15 sums greater than seven and there are 36 possible pairs altogether.

There are three matching pairs greater than seven.

$$P(B) = \frac{15}{36}$$

$$P(A \text{ and } B) = \frac{3}{36}$$

$$P(A/B) = \frac{P(A \text{ and } B)}{P(B)}$$

$$P(A/B) = \frac{\frac{3}{36}}{\frac{15}{36}} \text{ or } \frac{1}{5}$$

The conditional probability is $\frac{1}{5}$.

A card is drawn from a standard deck of 52 and is found to be red. Given that event, find each of the following probabilities.

1. $P(\text{heart})$

2. $P(\text{ace})$

3. $P(\text{face card})$

4. $P(\text{jack or ten})$

5. $P(\text{six of spades})$

6. $P(\text{six of hearts})$

A sports survey taken at Stirers High School shows that 48% of the respondents liked soccer, 66% liked basketball, and 38% liked hockey. Also, 30% liked soccer and basketball, 22% liked basketball and hockey and 28% liked soccer and hockey. Finally, 12% liked all three sports. Find each of the following probabilities.

7. The probability Meg likes soccer if she likes basketball.

8. The probability Biff likes basketball if he likes soccer.

9. The probability Muffy likes hockey if she likes basketball.

10. The probability Greg likes hockey and basketball if he likes soccer.

90

Enrichment

Conditional Probability

Suppose a pair of dice is thrown. It is known that the sum is greater than seven. Find the probability that the dice match.

The probability of an event given the occurrence of another event is called *conditional probability*. The conditional probability of event A, the dice match, given event B, their sum is greater than seven, is denoted $P(A/B)$.

There are 15 sums greater than seven and there are 36 possible pairs altogether.

There are three matching pairs greater than seven.

$$P(B) = \frac{15}{36}$$

$$P(A \text{ and } B) = \frac{3}{36}$$

$$P(A/B) = \frac{P(A \text{ and } B)}{P(B)}$$

$$P(A/B) = \frac{\frac{3}{36}}{\frac{15}{36}} \text{ or } \frac{1}{5}$$

The conditional probability is $\frac{1}{5}$.

A card is drawn from a standard deck of 52 and is found to be red. Given that event, find each of the following probabilities.

1. P(heart) $\frac{1}{2}$

2. P(ace) $\frac{1}{13}$

3. P(face card) $\frac{3}{13}$

4. P(jack or ten) $\frac{2}{13}$

5. P(six of spades) 0

6. P(six of hearts) $\frac{1}{26}$

A sports survey taken at Stirers High School shows that 48% of the respondents liked soccer, 66% liked basketball, and 38% liked hockey. Also, 30% liked soccer and basketball, 22% liked basketball and hockey and 28% liked soccer and hockey. Finally, 12% liked all three sports. Find each of the following probabilities.

7. The probability Meg likes soccer if she likes basketball. $\frac{30}{66}$ or $\frac{5}{11}$

8. The probability Biff likes basketball if he likes soccer. $\frac{30}{48}$ or $\frac{5}{8}$

9. The probability Muffy likes hockey if she likes basketball. $\frac{22}{66}$ or $\frac{1}{3}$

10. The probability Greg likes hockey and basketball if he likes soccer. $\frac{12}{48}$ or $\frac{1}{4}$

Enrichment

The Harmonic Mean

The *harmonic mean*, H, is a useful measure of central tendency in special cases of averaging rates.

Example: Recently Kendra and Bill took a trip of 370 miles and shared the driving. Kendra drove two hours at a rate of 30 mph and then drove the next 100 miles on a freeway at 55 mph. Then Bill drove the next two hours at 30 mph and he drove the last 100 miles on a freeway at 55 mph. What was the average speed of each driver?

Kendra drove the same length of time on both portions of her driving, so her average speed is the mean of the two rates. Her average speed was $\dfrac{30 + 55}{2}$ or 42.5 mph.

On the other hand, Bill drove the same distance on both portions of his driving, but the two lengths of time varied. Actually, the time he drove was $\dfrac{100}{30} + \dfrac{100}{55}$, or approximately 5.15 hours. His average speed was $\dfrac{200}{5.15}$, or about 38.8 mph.

Bill's average speed may be found by using the formula for the harmonic mean as follows.

Let n = number of rates x_i where $1 \le i \le n$. $\qquad H = \dfrac{n}{\sum\limits_{i=1}^{n} \dfrac{1}{x_i}}$

We apply the formula to Bill's speeds. $\qquad H = \dfrac{2}{\dfrac{1}{30} + \dfrac{1}{55}}$

$$H \approx 38.8 \text{ mph}$$

The mean, also called the arithmetic mean, is used when equal times are involved. When equal distances are involved, the harmonic mean is used.

Find the harmonic mean of each set of data. Round each answer to the nearest hundredth.

1. {3, 4, 5, 6}

2. {5, 10, 15, 20, 25}

3. Bev, Phyllis, and Gordon competed in a 375-mile relay race. Bev drove 40 mph, Phyllis drove 50 mph, and Gordon drove 60 mph. If each drove 125 miles, find the average driving speed of the contestants.

The Harmonic Mean

The *harmonic mean*, H, is a useful measure of central tendency in special cases of averaging rates.

Example: Recently Kendra and Bill took a trip of 370 miles and shared the driving. Kendra drove two hours at a rate of 30 mph and then drove the next 100 miles on a freeway at 55 mph. Then Bill drove the next two hours at 30 mph and he drove the last 100 miles on a freeway at 55 mph. What was the average speed of each driver?

Kendra drove the same length of time on both portions of her driving, so her average speed is the mean of the two rates. Her average speed was $\frac{30 + 55}{2}$ or 42.5 mph.

On the other hand, Bill drove the same distance on both portions of his driving, but the two lengths of time varied. Actually, the time he drove was $\frac{100}{30} + \frac{100}{55}$, or approximately 5.15 hours. His average speed was $\frac{200}{5.15}$, or about 38.8 mph.

Bill's average speed may be found by using the formula for the harmonic mean as follows.

Let n = number of rates x_i where $1 \le i \le n$. $\qquad H = \dfrac{n}{\sum\limits_{i=1}^{n} \frac{1}{x_i}}$

We apply the formula to Bill's speeds. $\qquad H = \dfrac{2}{\frac{1}{30} + \frac{1}{55}}$

$$H \approx 38.8 \text{ mph}$$

The mean, also called the arithmetic mean, is used when equal times are involved. When equal distances are involved, the harmonic mean is used.

Find the harmonic mean of each set of data. Round each answer to the nearest hundredth.

1. {3, 4, 5, 6} **4.21**

2. {5, 10, 15, 20, 25} **10.95**

3. Bev, Phyllis, and Gordon competed in a 375-mile relay race. Bev drove 40 mph, Phyllis drove 50 mph, and Gordon drove 60 mph. If each drove 125 miles, find the average driving speed of the contestants. **48.65 mph**

Enrichment

The Angle of Repose

Suppose you place a block of wood on an inclined plane, as shown at the right. If the angle, θ, at which the plane is inclined from the horizontal is very small, the block will not move. If you increase the angle, the block will eventually overcome the force of friction and start to slide down the plane.

At the instant the block begins to slide, the angle formed by the plane is called the angle of friction, or the angle of repose.

For situations in which the block and plane are smooth but unlubricated, the angle of repose depends *only* on the types of materials in the block and the plane. The angle is independent of the area of contact between the two surfaces and of the weight of the block.

The drawing at the right shows how to use vectors to find a coefficient of friction. This coefficient varies with different materials and is denoted by the Greek leter mu, μ.

$$F = W \sin\theta \qquad N = W \cos\theta$$
$$F = \mu N$$
$$\mu = \frac{\sin\theta}{\cos\theta} = \tan\theta$$

Solve each problem.

1. A wooden chute is built so that wooden crates can slide down into the basement of a store. What angle should the chute make for the crates to slide down at a constant speed?

Material	Coefficient of Friction μ
Wood on wood	0.5
Wood on stone	0.5
Rubber tire on dry concrete	1.0
Rubber tire on wet concrete	0.7

2. Will a 100-pound wooden crate slide down a stone ramp that makes an angle of 20° with the horizontal? Explain your answer.

3. If you increase the weight of the crate in Exercise 2 to 300 pounds, does it change your answer?

4. A car with rubber tires is being driven on dry concrete pavement. If the car tires spin without traction on a hill, how steep is the hill?

5. For Exercise 4, does it make a difference if it starts to rain? Explain your answer.

The Angle of Repose

Suppose you place a block of wood on an inclined plane, as shown at the right. If the angle, θ, at which the plane is inclined from the horizontal is very small, the block will not move. If you increase the angle, the block will eventually overcome the force of friction and start to slide down the plane.

At the instant the block begins to slide, the angle formed by the plane is called the angle of friction, or the angle of repose.

For situations in which the block and plane are smooth but unlubricated, the angle of repose depends *only* on the types of materials in the block and the plane. The angle is independent of the area of contact between the two surfaces and of the weight of the block.

The drawing at the right shows how to use vectors to find a coefficient of friction. This coefficient varies with different materials and is denoted by the Greek leter mu, μ.

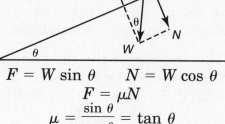

$$F = W \sin \theta \qquad N = W \cos \theta$$
$$F = \mu N$$
$$\mu = \frac{\sin \theta}{\cos \theta} = \tan \theta$$

Solve each problem.

1. A wooden chute is built so that wooden crates can slide down into the basement of a store. What angle should the chute make for the crates to slide down at a constant speed?
   27°

Material	Coefficient of Friction μ
Wood on wood	0.5
Wood on stone	0.5
Rubber tire on dry concrete	1.0
Rubber tire on wet concrete	0.7

2. Will a 100-pound wooden crate slide down a stone ramp that makes an angle of 20° with the horizontal? Explain your answer.
   No, the angle must be at least 27°.

3. If you increase the weight of the crate in Exercise 2 to 300 pounds, does it change your answer?
   No, the weight does not affect the angle.

4. A car with rubber tires is being driven on dry concrete pavement. If the car tires spin without traction on a hill, how steep is the hill?
   at least 45°

5. For Exercise 4, does it make a difference if it starts to rain? Explain your answer.
   Yes, the street needs to be only 35° for the car tires to spin.

Enrichment

Making and Using a Hypsometer

A **hypsometer** is a device that can be used to measure the height of an object. To construct your own hypsometer, you will need a rectangular piece of heavy cardboard that is at least 7 cm by 10 cm, a straw, transparent tape, a string about 20 cm long, and a small weight that can be attached to the string.

Mark off 1-cm increments along one short side and one long side of the cardboard. Tape the straw to the other short side. Then attach the weight to one end of the string, and attach the other end of the string to one corner of the cardboard, as shown in the figure below. The diagram below shows how your hypsometer should look.

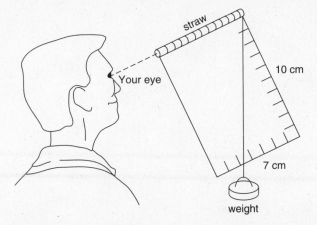

To use the hypsometer, you will need to measure the distance from the base of the object whose height you are finding to where you stand when you use the hypsometer.

Sight the top of the object through the straw. Note where the free-hanging string crosses the bottom scale. Then use similar triangles to find the height of the object.

1. Draw a diagram to illustrate how you can use similar triangles and the hypsometer to find the height of a tall object.

Use your hypsometer to find the height of each of the following.

2. your school's flagpole

3. a tree on your school's property

4. the highest point on the front wall of your school building

5. the goal posts on a football field

6. the hoop on a basketball court

NAME_____ DATE _____

Enrichment

Making and Using a Hypsometer

A **hypsometer** is a device that can be used to measure the height of an object. To construct your own hypsometer, you will need a rectangular piece of heavy cardboard that is at least 7 cm by 10 cm, a straw, transparent tape, a string about 20 cm long, and a small weight that can be attached to the string.

Mark off 1-cm increments along one short side and one long side of the cardboard. Tape the straw to the other short side. Then attach the weight to one end of the string, and attach the other end of the string to one corner of the cardboard, as shown in the figure below. The diagram below shows how your hypsometer should look.

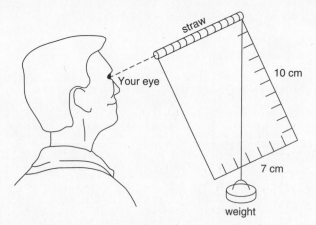

To use the hypsometer, you will need to measure the distance from the base of the object whose height you are finding to where you stand when you use the hypsometer.

Sight the top of the object through the straw. Note where the free-hanging string crosses the bottom scale. Then use similar triangles to find the height of the object.

1. Draw a diagram to illustrate how you can use similar triangles and the hypsometer to find the height of a tall object. **See students' diagrams.**

Use your hypsometer to find the height of each of the following.

See students' work.

2. your school's flagpole

3. a tree on your school's property

4. the highest point on the front wall of your school building

5. the goal posts on a football field

6. the hoop on a basketball court

© Glencoe/McGraw-Hill

T93

Algebra 2

Student Edition
Pages 786–791

13-3

Enrichment

Areas of Polygons and Circles

A regular polygon has sides of equal length and angles of equal measure. A regular polygon can be inscribed in or circumscribed about a circle. For n-sided regular polygons, the following area formulas can be used.

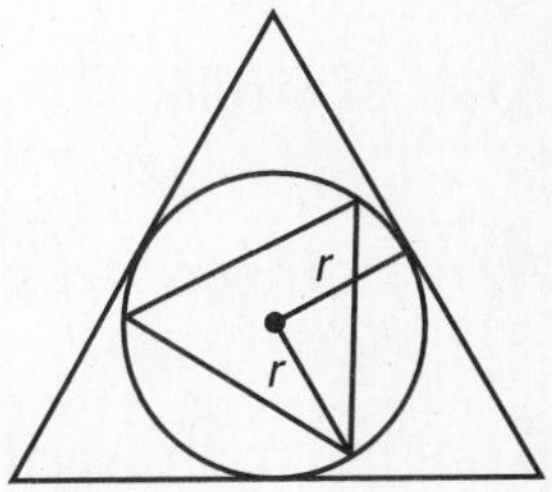

Area of circle $\qquad\qquad A_c = \pi r^2$

Area of inscribed polygon $\qquad A_I = \dfrac{nr^2}{2} \times \sin\dfrac{360°}{n}$

Area of circumscribed polygon $\qquad A_C = nr^2 \times \tan\dfrac{180°}{n}$

Use a calculator to complete the chart below for a unit circle (a circle of radius 1).

	Number of Sides	Area of Inscribed Polygon	Area Circle minus Area of Polygon	Area of Circumscribed Polygon	Area of Polygon minus Area of Circle
	3	1.2990381	1.8425545	5.1961524	2.054597
1.	4				
2.	8				
3.	12				
4.	20				
5.	24				
6.	28				
7.	32				
8.	1000				

9. What number do the areas of the circumscribed and inscribed polygons seem to be approaching?

Algebra 2

Enrichment

Student Edition
Pages 786–791

Areas of Polygons and Circles

A regular polygon has sides of equal length and angles of equal measure. A regular polygon can be inscribed in or circumscribed about a circle. For n-sided regular polygons, the following area formulas can be used.

Area of circle $\qquad A_C = \pi r^2$

Area of inscribed polygon $\qquad A_I = \dfrac{nr^2}{2} \times \sin \dfrac{360°}{n}$

Area of circumscribed polygon $\qquad A_C = nr^2 \times \tan \dfrac{180°}{n}$

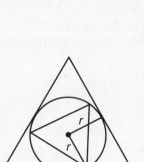

Use a calculator to complete the chart below for a unit circle (a circle of radius 1).

	Number of Sides	Area of Inscribed Polygon	Area Circle minus Area of Polygon	Area of Circumscribed Polygon	Area of Polygon minus Area of Circle
	3	1.2990381	1.8425545	5.1961524	2.054597
1.	4	2	1.1415927	4	0.8584073
2.	8	2.8284271	0.3131655	3.3137085	0.1721158
3.	12	3	0.1415926	3.2153903	0.0737977
4.	20	3.0901699	0.0514227	3.1676888	0.0260961
5.	24	3.1058285	0.0357641	3.1596599	0.0180672
6.	28	3.1152931	0.0262996	3.1548423	0.0132496
7.	32	3.1214452	0.0201475	3.1517249	0.0101322
8.	1000	3.1415720	0.0000206	3.1416030	0.0000103

9. What number do the areas of the circumscribed and inscribed polygons seem to be approaching? π

Algebra 2

Navigation

The bearing of a boat is an angle showing the direction the boat is heading. Often, the angle is measured from north, but it can be measured from any of the four compass directions. At the right, the bearing of the boat is 155°. Or, it can be described as 25° east of south (S25°E).

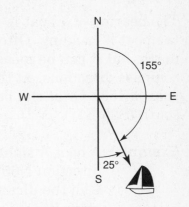

Example: A boat A sights the lighthouse B in the direction N65°E and the spire of a church C in the direction S75°E. According to the map, B is 7 miles from C in the direction N30°W. In order for A to avoid running aground, find the bearing it should keep to pass B at 4 miles distance.

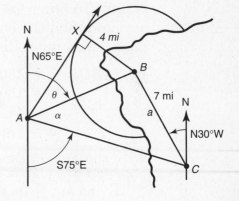

In $\triangle ABC$, $\angle \alpha = 180° - 65° - 75°$ or $40°$

$$\angle C = 180° - 30° - (180° - 75°)$$
$$= 45°$$
$$a = 7 \text{ miles}$$

With the Law of Sines,
$$AB = \frac{a \sin C}{\sin \alpha} = \frac{7(\sin 45°)}{\sin 40°} = 7.7 \text{ mi.}$$

The ray for the correct bearing for A must be tangent at X to circle B with radius $BX = 4$. Thus $\triangle ABX$ is a right triangle. Then $\sin \theta = \frac{BX}{AB} = \frac{4}{7.7} \approx 0.519$. Therefore, $\angle \theta = 31°18'$.

The bearing of A should be $65° - 31°18'$ or $33°42'$.

Solve the following.

1. Suppose the lighthouse B in the example is sighted at S30°W by a ship P due north of the church C. Find the bearing P should keep to pass B at 4 miles distance.

2. In the fog, the lighthouse keeper determines by radar that a boat 18 miles away is heading to the shore. The direction of the boat from the lighthouse is S80°E. What bearing should the lighthouse keeper radio the boat to take to come ashore 4 miles south of the lighthouse?

3. To avoid a rocky area along a shoreline, a ship at M travels 7 km to R, bearing 22°15', then 8 km to P, bearing 68°30', then 6 km to Q, bearing 109°15'. Find the distance from M to Q.

NAME_____ DATE_____

Enrichment

Navigation

The bearing of a boat is an angle showing the direction the boat is heading. Often, the angle is measured from north, but it can be measured from any of the four compass directions. At the right, the bearing of the boat is 155°. Or, it can be described as 25° east of south (S25°E).

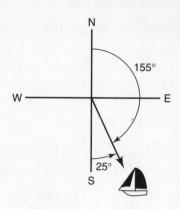

Example: A boat A sights the lighthouse B in the direction N65°E and the spire of a church C in the direction S75°E. According to the map, B is 7 miles from C in the direction N30°W. In order for A to avoid running aground, find the bearing it should keep to pass B at 4 miles distance.

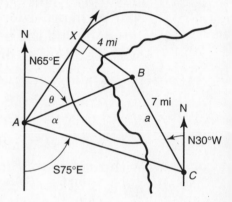

In $\triangle ABC$, $\angle \alpha = 180° - 65° - 75°$ or $40°$
$$\angle C = 180° - 30° - (180° - 75°)$$
$$= 45°$$
$$a = 7 \text{ miles}$$

With the Law of Sines,
$$AB = \frac{a \sin C}{\sin \alpha} = \frac{7(\sin 45°)}{\sin 40°} = 7.7 \text{ mi.}$$

The ray for the correct bearing for A must be tangent at X to circle B with radius $BX = 4$. Thus $\triangle ABX$ is a right triangle. Then $\sin \theta = \dfrac{BX}{AB} = \dfrac{4}{7.7} \approx 0.519$. Therefore, $\angle \theta = 31°18'$.

The bearing of A should be $65° - 31°18'$ or $33°42'$.

Solve the following.

1. Suppose the lighthouse B in the example is sighted at S30°W by a ship P due north of the church C. Find the bearing P should keep to pass B at 4 miles distance. **S64°51′ W**

2. In the fog, the lighthouse keeper determines by radar that a boat 18 miles away is heading to the shore. The direction of the boat from the lighthouse is S80°E. What bearing should the lighthouse keeper radio the boat to take to come ashore 4 miles south of the lighthouse? **S87.2°E**

3. To avoid a rocky area along a shoreline, a ship at M travels 7 km to R, bearing 22°15′, then 8 km to P, bearing 68°30′, then 6 km to Q, bearing 109°15′. Find the distance from M to Q. **17.4 km**

Enrichment

Student Edition
Pages 799–804

The Law of Cosines and the Pythagorean Theorem

The law of cosines bears strong similarities
to the Pythagorean theorem. According to
the law of cosines, if two sides of a triangle
have lengths a and b and if the angle
between them has a measure of $x°$, then the
length, y, of the third side of the triangle
can be found by using the equation

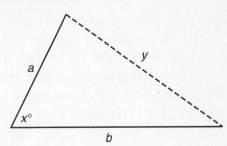

$$y^2 = a^2 + b^2 - 2ab \cos x°.$$

**Answer the following questions to clarify the relationship
between the law of cosines and the Pythagorean theorem.**

1. If the value of $x°$ becomes less and less, what number is $\cos x°$
   close to?

2. If the value of $x°$ is very close to zero but then increases, what
   happens to $\cos x°$ as $x°$ approaches 90°?

3. If $x°$ equals 90°, what is the value of $\cos x°$? What does the
   equation of $y^2 = a^2 + b^2 - 2ab \cos x°$ simplify to if $x°$ equals
   90°?

4. What happens to the value of $\cos x°$ as $x°$ increases beyond 90°
   and approaches 180°?

5. Consider some particular value of a and b, say 7 for a and 19
   for b. Use a graphing calculator to graph the equation you get
   by solving $y^2 = 7^2 + 19^2 - 2(7)(19) \cos x°$ for y.

   a. In view of the geometry of the situation, what range of
      values should you use for X?

   b. Display the graph and use the TRACE function. What do
      the maximum and minimum values appear to be for the
      function?

   c. How do the answers for Part b relate to the lengths 7 and
      19? Are the maximum and minimum values from Part b ever
      actually attained in the geometric situation?

NAME_____ DATE _____

Enrichment

Student Edition
Pages 799–804

The Law of Cosines and the Pythagorean Theorem

The law of cosines bears strong similarities
to the Pythagorean theorem. According to
the law of cosines, if two sides of a triangle
have lengths a and b and if the angle
between them has a measure of $x°$, then the
length, y, of the third side of the triangle
can be found by using the equation

$$y^2 = a^2 + b^2 - 2ab \cos x°.$$

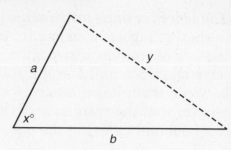

**Answer the following questions to clarify the relationship
between the law of cosines and the Pythagorean theorem.**

1. If the value of $x°$ becomes less and less, what number is $\cos x°$
   close to? **1**

2. If the value of $x°$ is very close to zero but then increases, what
   happens to $\cos x°$ as $x°$ approaches 90°? **decreases,
   approaches 0**

3. If $x°$ equals 90°, what is the value of $\cos x°$? What does the
   equation of $y^2 = a^2 + b^2 - 2ab \cos x°$ simplify to if $x°$ equals
   90°? **0, $y^2 = a^2 + b^2$**

4. What happens to the value of $\cos x°$ as $x°$ increases beyond 90°
   and approaches 180°? **decreases to −1**

5. Consider some particular value of a and b, say 7 for a and 19
   for b. Use a graphing calculator to graph the equation you get
   by solving $y^2 = 7^2 + 19^2 - 2(7)(19) \cos x°$ for y.
   See students' graphs.

   a. In view of the geometry of the situation, what range of
      values should you use for X? **X min = 0°; X max = 180°**

   b. Display the graph and use the TRACE function. What do
      the maximum and minimum values appear to be for the
      function? **See students' graphs.**

   c. How do the answers for Part b relate to the lengths 7 and
      19? Are the maximum and minimum values from Part b ever
      actually attained in the geometric situation?
      min = 19 − 7; max = 19 + 7; no

13-6

Enrichment

Polar Coordinates

Consider an angle in standard position with its vertex at a point O called the *pole*. Its initial side is on a coordinated axis called the *polar axis*. A point P on the terminal side of the angle is named by the *polar coordinates* (r, θ) where r is the directed distance of the point from O and θ is the measure of the angle.

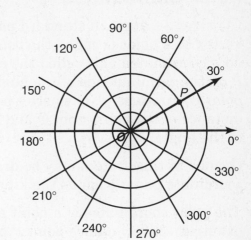

Graphs in this system may be drawn on polar coordinate paper such as the kind shown at the right.

The polar coordinates of a point are not unique. For example, $(3, 30°)$ names point P as well as $(3, 390°)$. Another name for P is $(-3, 210°)$. Can you see why? The coordinates of the pole are $(0, \theta)$ where θ may be any angle.

Example: Draw the graph of the function $r = \cos \theta$.
Make a table of convenient values for θ and r.
Then plot the points.

θ	0°	30°	60°	90°	120°	150°	180°
r	1	$\dfrac{\sqrt{3}}{2}$	$\dfrac{1}{2}$	0	$-\dfrac{1}{2}$	$-\dfrac{\sqrt{3}}{2}$	-1

Since the period of the cosine function is 180°, values of r for $\theta > 180°$ are repeated.

Graph each function by making a table of values and plotting the values on polar coordinate paper.

1. $r = 4$

2. $r = 3 \sin \theta$

3. $r = 3 \cos 2\theta$

4. $r = 2(1 + \cos \theta)$

Enrichment

Polar Coordinates

Consider an angle in standard position with its
vertex at a point O called the *pole*. Its initial side is
on a coordinated axis called the *polar axis*. A point
P on the terminal side of the angle is named by the
polar coordinates (r, θ) where r is the directed
distance of the point from O and θ is the measure
of the angle.

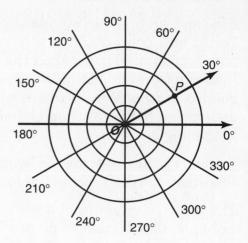

Graphs in this system may be drawn on polar
coordinate paper such as the kind shown at the right.

The polar coordinates of a point are not unique. For
example, $(3, 30°)$ names point P as well as $(3, 390°)$.
Another name for P is $(-3, 210°)$. Can you see why?
The coordinates of the pole are $(0, \theta)$ where θ may be
any angle.

Example: Draw the graph of the function $r = \cos \theta$.
Make a table of convenient values for θ and r.
Then plot the points.

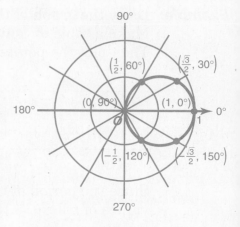

θ	0°	30°	60°	90°	120°	150°	180°
r	1	$\dfrac{\sqrt{3}}{2}$	$\dfrac{1}{2}$	0	$-\dfrac{1}{2}$	$-\dfrac{\sqrt{3}}{2}$	-1

Since the period of the cosine function is 180°,
values of r for $\theta > 180°$ are repeated.

**Graph each function by making a table of values and plotting
the values on polar coordinate paper.**

1. $r = 4$

$r = 4$ for all values of θ. Graph
should be a circle with radius 4
and center at the pole.

2. $r = 3 \sin \theta$

Graph is circle of radius $\dfrac{3}{2}$ with
center at $\left(\dfrac{3}{2}, 90°\right)$.

3. $r = 3 \cos 2\theta$

Graph looks like flower with 4
petals, points of petals are at
$(3, 0°)$, $(3, 90°)$, $(3, 180°)$, $(3, 270°)$.
All petals meet at pole.

4. $r = 2(1 + \cos \theta)$

Graph is heart-shaped curve,
symmetric with respect to polar
axis.

Snell's Law

Snell's Law describes what happens to a ray of light that passes from air into water or some other substance. In the figure, the ray starts at the left and makes an angle of incidence θ with the surface.

Part of the ray is reflected, creating an angle of reflection θ. The rest of the ray is bent, or refracted, as it passes through the other medium. This creates angle θ'.

The angle of incidence equals the angle of reflection.

The angles of incidence and refraction are related by Snell's Law:

$$\sin \theta = k \sin \theta'$$

The constant k is called the index of refraction.

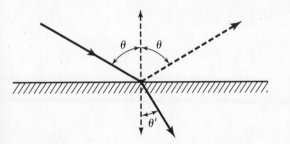

k	Substance
1.33	Water
1.36	Ethyl alcohol
1.54	Rock salt and Quartz
1.46-1.96	Glass
2.42	Diamond

Use Snell's Law to solve the following. Round angle measures to the nearest tenth of a degree.

1. If the angle of incidence at which a ray of light strikes the surface of a window is 45° and $k = 1.6$, what is the measure of the angle of refraction?

2. If the angle of incidence of a ray of light that strikes the surface of water is 50°, what is the angle of refraction?

3. If the angle of refraction of a ray of light striking a quartz crystal is 24°, what is the angle of incidence?

4. The angles of incidence and refraction for rays of light were measured five times for a certain substance. The measurements (one of which was in error) are shown in the table. Was the substance glass, quartz, or diamond?

θ	15°	30°	40°	60°	80°
θ'	9.7°	16.1°	21.2°	28.6°	33.2°

5. If the angle of incidence at which a ray of light strikes the surface of ethyl alcohol is 60°, what is the angle of refraction?

Enrichment

Snell's Law

Snell's Law describes what happens to a ray of light that passes from air into water or some other substance. In the figure, the ray starts at the left and makes an angle of incidence θ with the surface.

Part of the ray is reflected, creating an angle of reflection θ. The rest of the ray is bent, or refracted, as it passes through the other medium. This creates angle θ'.

The angle of incidence equals the angle of reflection.

The angles of incidence and refraction are related by Snell's Law:

$$\sin \theta = k \sin \theta'$$

The constant k is called the index of refraction.

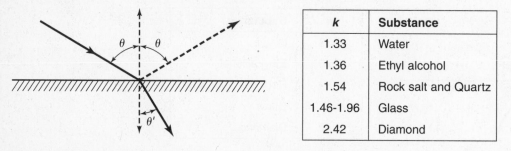

k	Substance
1.33	Water
1.36	Ethyl alcohol
1.54	Rock salt and Quartz
1.46-1.96	Glass
2.42	Diamond

Use Snell's Law to solve the following. Round angle measures to the nearest tenth of a degree.

1. If the angle of incidence at which a ray of light strikes the surface of a window is 45° and $k = 1.6$, what is the measure of the angle of refraction? **26.2°**

2. If the angle of incidence of a ray of light that strikes the surface of water is 50°, what is the angle of refraction? **35.2°**

3. If the angle of refraction of a ray of light striking a quartz crystal is 24°, what is the angle of incidence? **38.8°**

4. The angles of incidence and refraction for rays of light were measured five times for a certain substance. The measurements (one of which was in error) are shown in the table. Was the substance glass, quartz, or diamond? **glass**

θ	15°	30°	40°	60°	80°
θ'	9.7°	16.1°	21.2°	28.6°	33.2°

5. If the angle of incidence at which a ray of light strikes the surface of ethyl alcohol is 60°, what is the angle of refraction? **39.6°**

Algebra 2

NAME_____ DATE _____

Enrichment

Blueprints

Interpreting blueprints requires the ability to select and use trigonometric functions and geometric properties. The figure below represents a plan for an improvement to a roof. The metal fitting shown makes a 30° angle with the horizontal. The vertices of the geometric shapes are *not* labeled in these plans. Relevant information must be selected and the appropriate function used to find the unknown measures.

Example: Find the unknown measures in the figure at the right.

The measures x and y are the legs of a right triangle.
The measure of the hypotenuse is $\frac{15}{16}$ in. + $\frac{5}{16}$ in. or $\frac{20}{16}$ in.

$$\frac{y}{\frac{20}{16}} = \cos 30°$$

$$\frac{x}{\frac{20}{16}} = \sin 30°$$

$y = 1.08$ in. $x = 0.63$ in.

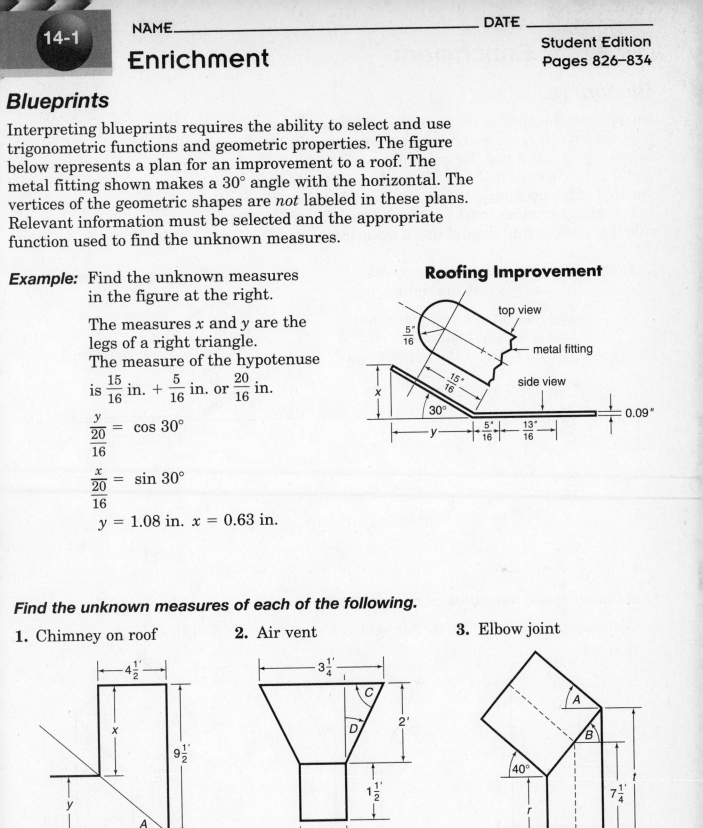

Roofing Improvement

Find the unknown measures of each of the following.

1. Chimney on roof

2. Air vent

3. Elbow joint

99

14-1

Enrichment

Student Edition
Pages 826–834

Blueprints

Interpreting blueprints requires the ability to select and use trigonometric functions and geometric properties. The figure below represents a plan for an improvement to a roof. The metal fitting shown makes a 30° angle with the horizontal. The vertices of the geometric shapes are *not* labeled in these plans. Relevant information must be selected and the appropriate function used to find the unknown measures.

Example: Find the unknown measures in the figure at the right.

The measures x and y are the legs of a right triangle.
The measure of the hypotenuse is $\frac{15}{16}$ in. $+ \frac{5}{16}$ in. or $\frac{20}{16}$ in.

$$\frac{y}{\frac{20}{16}} = \cos 30°$$

$$\frac{x}{\frac{20}{16}} = \sin 30°$$

$y = 1.08$ in. $x = 0.63$ in.

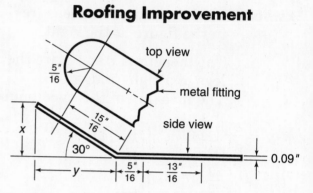

Roofing Improvement

top view

metal fitting

side view

$\frac{5}{16}$

$\frac{15}{16}$

x

30°

y

$\frac{5"}{16}$

$\frac{13"}{16}$

0.09"

Find the unknown measures of each of the following.

1. Chimney on roof

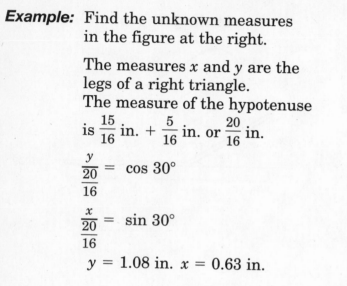

$4\frac{1}{2}'$

x

$9\frac{1}{2}'$

y

A

40°

$y = 3.78'$
$x = 5.72'$
$\angle A = 40°$

2. Air vent

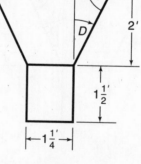

$3\frac{1}{4}'$

C

D

2'

$1\frac{1}{2}'$

$1\frac{1}{4}'$

$\angle C = 63.43°$
$\angle D = 26.57°$

3. Elbow joint

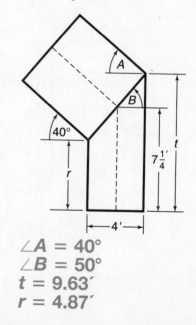

A

B

40°

r

$7\frac{1}{4}'$

t

4'

$\angle A = 40°$
$\angle B = 50°$
$t = 9.63'$
$r = 4.87'$

Algebra 2

Enrichment

Heron's Formula

Heron's formula can be used to find the area of a triangle if you
know the lengths of the three sides. Consider any triangle ABC.
Let K represent the area of $\triangle ABC$. Then

$$K = \frac{1}{2}\,bc\,\sin A$$

$$K^2 = \frac{b^2c^2\sin^2 A}{4} \qquad \textbf{Square both sides.}$$

$$= \frac{b^2c^2(1 - \cos^2 A)}{4}$$

$$= \frac{b^2c^2(1 + \cos A)(1 - \cos A)}{4}$$

$$= \frac{b^2c^2}{4}\left(1 + \frac{b^2 + c^2 - a^2}{2bc}\right)\left(1 - \frac{b^2 + c^2 - a^2}{2bc}\right) \qquad \textbf{Use the law of cosines.}$$

$$= \frac{b + c + a}{2}\cdot\frac{b + c - a}{2}\cdot\frac{a + b - c}{2}\cdot\frac{a - b + c}{2} \qquad \textbf{Simplify.}$$

Let $s = \dfrac{a + b + c}{2}$. Then $s - a = \dfrac{b + c - a}{2},\ s - b = \dfrac{a + c - b}{2},\ s - c = \dfrac{a + b - c}{2}.$

$$K^2 = s(s - a)(s - b)(s - c) \qquad \textbf{Substitute.}$$

$$K = \sqrt{s(s - a)(s - b)(s - c)}$$

Heron's Formula	The area of $\triangle ABC$ is $\sqrt{s(s - a)(s - b)(s - c)}$, where $s = \dfrac{a + b + c}{2}$.

Use Heron's formula to find the area of $\triangle ABC$.

1. $a = 3, b = 4.4, c = 7$

2. $a = 8.2, b = 10.3, c = 9.5$

3. $a = 31.3, b = 92.0, c = 67.9$

4. $a = 0.54, b = 1.32, c = 0.78$

5. $a = 321, b = 178, c = 298$

6. $a = 0.05, b = 0.08, c = 0.04$

7. $a = 21.5, b = 33.0, c = 41.7$

8. $a = 2.08, b = 9.13, c = 8.99$

NAME_____ DATE _____

Enrichment

Heron's Formula

Heron's formula can be used to find the area of a triangle if you know the lengths of the three sides. Consider any triangle ABC. Let K represent the area of $\triangle ABC$. Then

$$K = \frac{1}{2}\, bc \sin A$$

$$K^2 = \frac{b^2 c^2 \sin^2 A}{4} \qquad \textbf{Square both sides.}$$

$$= \frac{b^2 c^2 (1 - \cos^2 A)}{4}$$

$$= \frac{b^2 c^2 (1 + \cos A)(1 - \cos A)}{4}$$

$$= \frac{b^2 c^2}{4}\left(1 + \frac{b^2 + c^2 - a^2}{2bc}\right)\left(1 - \frac{b^2 + c^2 - a^2}{2bc}\right) \qquad \textbf{Use the law of cosines.}$$

$$= \frac{b + c + a}{2} \cdot \frac{b + c - a}{2} \cdot \frac{a + b - c}{2} \cdot \frac{a - b + c}{2} \qquad \textbf{Simplify.}$$

Let $s = \dfrac{a + b + c}{2}$. Then $s - a = \dfrac{b + c - a}{2}$, $s - b = \dfrac{a + c - b}{2}$, $s - c = \dfrac{a + b - c}{2}$.

$$K^2 = s(s - a)(s - b)(s - c) \qquad \textbf{Substitute.}$$

$$K = \sqrt{s(s - a)(s - b)(s - c)}$$

Heron's Formula	The area of $\triangle ABC$ is $\sqrt{s(s - a)(s - b)(s - c)}$, where $s = \dfrac{a + b + c}{2}$.

Use Heron's formula to find the area of $\triangle ABC$.

1. $a = 3, b = 4.4, c = 7$ **4.1**

2. $a = 8.2, b = 10.3, c = 9.5$ **36.8**

3. $a = 31.3, b = 92.0, c = 67.9$ **782.9**

4. $a = 0.54, b = 1.32, c = 0.78$ **no such triangle**

5. $a = 321, b = 178, c = 298$ **26,160.9**

6. $a = 0.05, b = 0.08, c = 0.04$ **0.00082**

7. $a = 21.5, b = 33.0, c = 41.7$ **351.6**

8. $a = 2.08, b = 9.13, c = 8.99$ **9.3**

Planetary Orbits

The orbit of a planet around the sun is
an ellipse with the sun at one focus. Let
the pole of a polar coordinate system be
that focus and the polar axis be toward
the other focus. The polar equation of an

ellipse is $r = \dfrac{2ep}{1 - e \cos \theta}$. Since $2p = \dfrac{b^2}{c}$ and

$b^2 = a^2 - c^2$, $2p = \dfrac{a^2 - c^2}{c} = \dfrac{a^2}{c}\left(1 - \dfrac{c^2}{a^2}\right)$.

Because $e = \dfrac{c}{a}$, $2p = a\left(\dfrac{a}{c}\right)\left(1 - \left(\dfrac{c}{a}\right)^2\right) = $

$a\left(\dfrac{1}{e}\right)(1 - e^2)$.

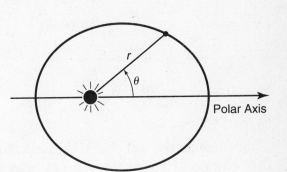

Therefore $2ep = a(1 - e^2)$. Substituting
into the polar equation of an ellipse yields
an equation that is useful for finding
distances from the planet to the sun.

$$r = \frac{a(1 - e^2)}{1 - e \cos \theta}$$

Note that e is the eccentricity of the orbit and a is the length of
the semi-major axis of the ellipse. Also, a is the mean distance
of the planet from the sun.

Example: The mean distance of Venus from the sun is $67.24 \times$
10^6 miles and the eccentricity of its orbit is .006788.
Find the minimum and maximum distances of Venus
from the sun.
The minimum distance occurs when $\theta = \pi$.

$$r = \frac{67.24 \times 10^6(1 - 0.006788^2)}{1 - 0.006788 \cos \pi} = 66.78 \times 10^6 \text{ miles}$$

The maximum distance occurs when $\theta = 0$.

$$r = \frac{67.24 \times 10^6(1 - 0.006788^2)}{1 - 0.006788 \cos 0} = 67.70 \times 10^6 \text{ miles}$$

Complete each of the following.

1. The mean distance of Mars from the sun is 141.64×10^6
   miles and the eccentricity of its orbit is 0.093382. Find the
   minimum and maximum distances of Mars from the sun.

2. The minimum distance of Earth from the sun is 91.445×10^6
   miles and the eccentricity of its orbit is 0.016734. Find the
   mean and maximum distances of Earth from the sun.

Planetary Orbits

The orbit of a planet around the sun is
an ellipse with the sun at one focus. Let
the pole of a polar coordinate system be
that focus and the polar axis be toward
the other focus. The polar equation of an
ellipse is $r = \dfrac{2ep}{1 - e \cos \theta}$. Since $2p = \dfrac{b^2}{c}$ and

$b^2 = a^2 - c^2$, $2p = \dfrac{a^2 - c^2}{c} = \dfrac{a^2}{c}\left(1 - \dfrac{c^2}{a^2}\right)$.

Because $e = \dfrac{c}{a}$, $2p = a\left(\dfrac{a}{c}\right)\left(1 - \left(\dfrac{c}{a}\right)^2\right) =$

$a\left(\dfrac{1}{e}\right)(1 - e^2)$.

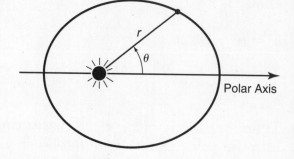

Therefore $2ep = a(1 - e^2)$. Substituting
into the polar equation of an ellipse yields
an equation that is useful for finding
distances from the planet to the sun.

$$r = \frac{a(1 - e^2)}{1 - e \cos \theta}$$

Note that e is the eccentricity of the orbit and a is the length of
the semi-major axis of the ellipse. Also, a is the mean distance
of the planet from the sun.

Example: The mean distance of Venus from the sun is 67.24×10^6 miles and the eccentricity of its orbit is .006788.
Find the minimum and maximum distances of Venus
from the sun.
The minimum distance occurs when $\theta = \pi$.

$$r = \frac{67.24 \times 10^6(1 - 0.006788^2)}{1 - 0.006788 \cos \pi} = 66.78 \times 10^6 \text{ miles}$$

The maximum distance occurs when $\theta = 0$.

$$r = \frac{67.24 \times 10^6(1 - 0.006788^2)}{1 - 0.006788 \cos 0} = 67.70 \times 10^6 \text{ miles}$$

Complete each of the following.

1. The mean distance of Mars from the sun is 141.64×10^6
   miles and the eccentricity of its orbit is 0.093382. Find the
   minimum and maximum distances of Mars from the sun.
   max. dist. = 15.49×10^7 mi   **min. dist. = 12.84×10^7 mi**

2. The minimum distance of Earth from the sun is 91.445×10^6
   miles and the eccentricity of its orbit is 0.016734. Find the
   mean and maximum distances of Earth from the sun.
   max. dist. = 93.00×10^6 mi   **mean dist. = 91.47×10^6 mi**

Enrichment

Translating Graphs of Trigonometric Functions

Three graphs are shown at the right:

$$y = 3 \sin 2\theta$$

$$y = 3 \sin 2(\theta - 30°)$$

$$y + 4 = 3 \sin 2\theta$$

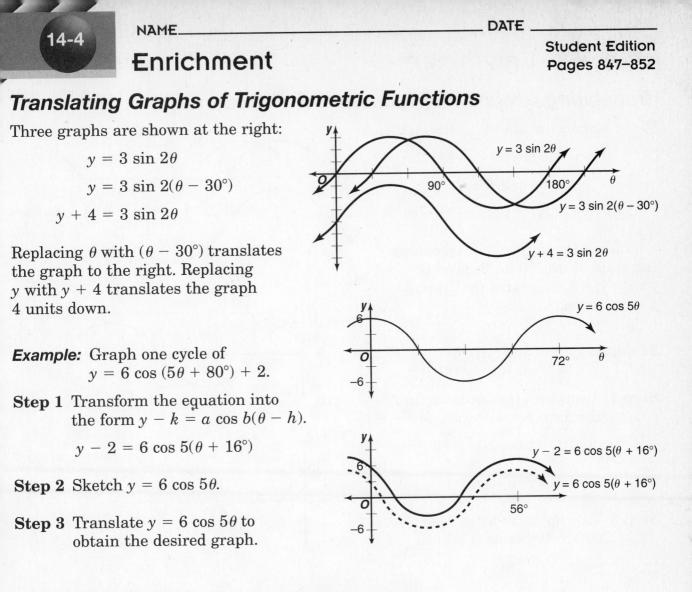

Replacing θ with $(\theta - 30°)$ translates the graph to the right. Replacing y with $y + 4$ translates the graph 4 units down.

Example: Graph one cycle of
$$y = 6 \cos (5\theta + 80°) + 2.$$

Step 1 Transform the equation into the form $y - k = a \cos b(\theta - h)$.

$$y - 2 = 6 \cos 5(\theta + 16°)$$

Step 2 Sketch $y = 6 \cos 5\theta$.

Step 3 Translate $y = 6 \cos 5\theta$ to obtain the desired graph.

Sketch these graphs on the same coordinate system.

1. $y = 3 \sin 2(\theta + 45°)$ **2.** $y - 1 = 3 \sin 2\theta$ **3.** $y + 5 = 3 \sin 2(\theta + 90°)$

Graph one cycle of each curve.

4. $y = 2 \sin 4(\theta - 50°)$ **5.** $y = 5 \sin (3\theta + 90°)$

6. $y = 6 \cos (4\theta + 360°) + 3$ **7.** $y = 6 \cos 4\theta + 3$

8. The graphs for problems 6 and 7 should be the same. Use the sum formula for cosine of a sum to show that the equations are equivalent.

       Algebra 2

Enrichment

Translating Graphs of Trigonometric Functions

Three graphs are shown at the right:

$$y = 3 \sin 2\theta$$

$$y = 3 \sin 2(\theta - 30°)$$

$$y + 4 = 3 \sin 2\theta$$

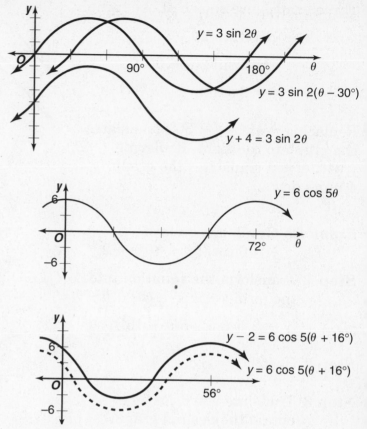

Replacing θ with $(\theta - 30°)$ translates the graph to the right. Replacing y with $y + 4$ translates the graph 4 units down.

Example: Graph one cycle of
$$y = 6 \cos (5\theta + 80°) + 2.$$

Step 1 Transform the equation into the form $y - k = a \cos b(\theta - h)$.

$$y - 2 = 6 \cos 5(\theta + 16°)$$

Step 2 Sketch $y = 6 \cos 5\theta$.

Step 3 Translate $y = 6 \cos 5\theta$ to obtain the desired graph.

Sketch these graphs on the same coordinate system. See students' graphs.

1. $y = 3 \sin 2(\theta + 45°)$ **2.** $y - 1 = 3 \sin 2\theta$ **3.** $y + 5 = 3 \sin 2(\theta + 90°)$

Graph one cycle of each curve. See students' graphs.

4. $y = 2 \sin 4(\theta - 50°)$ **5.** $y = 5 \sin (3\theta + 90°)$

6. $y = 6 \cos (4\theta + 360°) + 3$ **7.** $y = 6 \cos 4\theta + 3$

8. The graphs for problems 6 and 7 should be the same. Use the sum formula for cosine of a sum to show that the equations are equivalent.

$$\cos (4\theta + 360°) = (\cos 4\theta)(\cos 360°) - (\sin 4\theta)(\sin 360°)$$
$$= (\cos 4\theta)(1) - (\sin 4\theta)(0)$$
$$= \cos 4\theta$$

So, $y = 6 \cos (4\theta + 360°) + 3$ and $y = 6 \cos 4\theta + 3$ are equivalent.

Enrichment

Identities for the Products of Sines and Cosines

By adding the identities for the sines of the sum and difference of the measures of two angles, a new identity is obtained.

$$\sin (\alpha + \beta) = \sin \alpha \cos \beta + \cos \alpha \sin \beta$$
$$\sin (\alpha - \beta) = \sin \alpha \cos \beta - \cos \alpha \sin \beta$$
$$(i) \quad \sin (\alpha + \beta) + \sin (\alpha - \beta) = 2 \sin \alpha \cos \beta$$

This new identity is useful for expressing certain products as sums.

Example: Write $\sin 3\theta \cos \theta$ as a sum.
In the identity let $\alpha = 3\theta$ and $\beta = \theta$ so that
$2 \sin 3\theta \cos \theta = \sin (3\theta + \theta) + \sin (3\theta - \theta)$. Thus,
$\sin 3\theta \cos \theta = \dfrac{1}{2}\sin 4\theta + \dfrac{1}{2}\sin 2\theta$.

By subtracting the identities for $\sin (\alpha + \beta)$ and $\sin (\alpha - \beta)$, a similar identity for expressing a product as a difference is obtained.

$$(ii) \; \sin (\alpha + \beta) - \sin (\alpha - \beta) = 2 \cos \alpha \sin \beta$$

Complete.

1. Use the identities for $\cos (\alpha + \beta)$ and $\cos (\alpha - \beta)$ to find identities for expressing the products $2 \cos \alpha \cos \beta$ and $2 \sin \alpha \sin \beta$ as a sum or difference.

2. Find the value of $\sin 105° \cos 75°$ without using tables.

3. Express $\cos \theta \sin \dfrac{\theta}{2}$ as a difference.

Enrichment

Identities for the Products of Sines and Cosines

By adding the identities for the sines of the sum and difference of the measures of two angles, a new identity is obtained.

$$\sin (\alpha + \beta) = \sin \alpha \cos \beta + \cos \alpha \sin \beta$$
$$\underline{\quad\quad \sin (\alpha - \beta) = \sin \alpha \cos \beta - \cos \alpha \sin \beta}$$
$$(i) \quad \sin (\alpha + \beta) + \sin (\alpha - \beta) = 2 \sin \alpha \cos \beta$$

This new identity is useful for expressing certain products as sums.

Example: Write $\sin 3\theta \cos \theta$ as a sum.

In the identity let $\alpha = 3\theta$ and $\beta = \theta$ so that
$2 \sin 3\theta \cos \theta = \sin (3\theta + \theta) + \sin (3\theta - \theta)$. Thus,
$\sin 3\theta \cos \theta = \dfrac{1}{2}\sin 4\theta + \dfrac{1}{2}\sin 2\theta$.

By subtracting the identities for $\sin (\alpha + \beta)$ and $\sin (\alpha - \beta)$, a similar identity for expressing a product as a difference is obtained.

$$(ii)\ \sin (\alpha + \beta) - \sin (\alpha - \beta) = 2 \cos \alpha \sin \beta$$

Complete.

1. Use the identities for $\cos (\alpha + \beta)$ and $\cos (\alpha - \beta)$ to find identities for expressing the products $2 \cos \alpha \cos \beta$ and $2 \sin \alpha \sin \beta$ as a sum or difference.

$2 \cos \alpha \cos \beta = \cos (\alpha + \beta) + \cos (\alpha - \beta)$
$2 \sin \alpha \sin \beta = \cos (\alpha - \beta) - \cos (\alpha + \beta)$

2. Find the value of $\sin 105° \cos 75°$ without using tables.

$\dfrac{1}{2}[\sin (105° + 75°) + \sin (105° - 75°)]$;

$\dfrac{1}{2}\left[0 + \dfrac{1}{2}\right]; \dfrac{1}{2} \cdot \dfrac{1}{2} = \dfrac{1}{4}$

3. Express $\cos \theta \sin \dfrac{\theta}{2}$ as a difference.

$2 \cos \theta \sin \dfrac{\theta}{2} = \sin \left(\theta + \dfrac{\theta}{2}\right) - \sin \left(\theta - \dfrac{\theta}{2}\right)$

$\cos \theta \sin \dfrac{\theta}{2} = \dfrac{1}{2} \sin \dfrac{3\theta}{2} - \dfrac{1}{2} \sin \dfrac{\theta}{2}$

Enrichment

Alternating Current

The figure at the right represents an alternating current generator. A rectangular coil of wire is suspended between the poles of a magnet. As the coil of wire is rotated, it passes through the magnetic field and generates current.

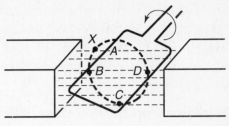

As point X on the coil passes through the points A and C, its motion is along the direction of the magnetic field between the poles. Therefore, no current is generated. However, through points B and D, the motion of X is perpendicular to the magnetic field. This induces maximum current in the coil. Between A and B, B and C, C and D, and D and A, the current in the coil will have an intermediate value. Thus, the graph of the current of an alternating current generator is closely related to the sine curve.

The maximum current may have a positive or negative value.

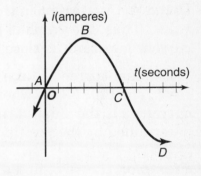

The actual current, i, in a household current is given by $i = I_M \sin(120\pi t + \alpha)$ where I_M is the maximum value of the current, t is the elapsed time in seconds, and α is the angle determined by the position of the coil at time t_n.

Example: If $\alpha = \dfrac{\pi}{2}$, find a value of t for which $i = 0$.

If $i = 0$, then $I_M \sin(120\pi t + \alpha) = 0$. $i = I_M \sin(120\pi t + \alpha)$
Since $I_M \neq 0$, $\sin(120\pi t + \alpha) = 0$.   **If $ab = 0$ and $a \neq 0$, then $b = 0$.**
Let $120\pi t + \alpha = s$. Thus, $\sin s = 0$.
$s = \pi$ because $\sin \pi = 0$.
$120\pi t + \alpha = \pi$ **Substitute $120\pi t + \alpha$ for s.**
$120\pi t + \dfrac{\pi}{2} = \pi$ **Substitute $\dfrac{\pi}{2}$ for α.**
$\phantom{120\pi t + \dfrac{\pi}{2}} = \dfrac{1}{240}$ **Solve for t.**

This solution is the first positive value of t that satisfies the problem.

Using the equation for the actual current in a household circuit, $i = I_M \sin(120\pi t + \alpha)$, solve each problem. For each problem, find the first positive value of t.

1. If $\alpha = 0$, find a value of t for which $i = 0$.

2. If $\alpha = 0$, find a value of t for which $i = +I_M$.

3. If $\alpha = \dfrac{\pi}{2}$, find a value of t for which $i = -I_M$.

4. If $\alpha = \dfrac{\pi}{4}$, find a value of t for which $i = 0$.

Enrichment

Alternating Current

The figure at the right represents an alternating current generator. A rectangular coil of wire is suspended between the poles of a magnet. As the coil of wire is rotated, it passes through the magnetic field and generates current.

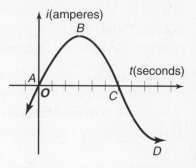

As point X on the coil passes through the points A and C, its motion is along the direction of the magnetic field between the poles. Therefore, no current is generated. However, through points B and D, the motion of X is perpendicular to the magnetic field. This induces maximum current in the coil. Between A and B, B and C, C and D, and D and A, the current in the coil will have an intermediate value. Thus, the graph of the current of an alternating current generator is closely related to the sine curve.

The maximum current may have a positive or negative value.

The actual current, i, in a household current is given by $i = I_M \sin(120\pi t + \alpha)$ where I_M is the maximum value of the current, t is the elapsed time in seconds, and α is the angle determined by the position of the coil at time t_n.

Example: If $\alpha = \dfrac{\pi}{2}$, find a value of t for which $i = 0$.

If $i = 0$, then $I_M \sin(120\pi t + \alpha) = 0$. $i = I_M \sin(120\pi t + \alpha)$

Since $I_M \neq 0$, $\sin(120\pi t + \alpha) = 0$.   If $ab = 0$ and $a \neq 0$, then $b = 0$.

Let $120\pi t + \alpha = s$. Thus, $\sin s = 0$.

$s = \pi$ because $\sin \pi = 0$.

$120\pi t + \alpha = \pi$ **Substitute $120\pi t + \alpha$ for s.**

$120\pi t + \dfrac{\pi}{2} = \pi$ **Substitute $\dfrac{\pi}{2}$ for α.**

$= \dfrac{1}{240}$ **Solve for t.**

This solution is the first positive value of t that satisfies the problem.

Using the equation for the actual current in a household circuit, $i = I_M \sin(120\pi t + \alpha)$, solve each problem. For each problem, find the first positive value of t.

1. If $\alpha = 0$, find a value of t for which $i = 0$.
   $t = \dfrac{1}{120}$

2. If $\alpha = 0$, find a value of t for which $i = +I_M$.
   $t = \dfrac{1}{240}$

3. If $\alpha = \dfrac{\pi}{2}$, find a value of t for which $i = -I_M$.
   $t = \dfrac{1}{120}$

4. If $\alpha = \dfrac{\pi}{4}$, find a value of t for which $i = 0$.
   $t = \dfrac{1}{160}$